Culture and Health

Custom Edition

Rodney D. Coates

Abby L. Ferber

David L. Brunsma

Compiled for: Marquette University HEAL 1025

Chapters Contributed From *The Matrix of Race:
Social Construction, Intersectionality, and Inequality* by
Rodney D. Coates, Abby L. Ferber, and David L. Brunsma

**SAGE**

Los Angeles | London | New Delhi
Singapore | Washington DC | Melbourne

FOR INFORMATION:

SAGE Publications, Inc.
2455 Teller Road
Thousand Oaks, California 91320
E-mail: order@sagepub.com

SAGE Publications Ltd.
1 Oliver's Yard
55 City Road
London EC1Y 1SP
United Kingdom

SAGE Publications India Pvt. Ltd.
B 1/I 1 Mohan Cooperative Industrial Area
Mathura Road, New Delhi 110 044
India

SAGE Publications Asia-Pacific Pte. Ltd.
3 Church Street
#10-04 Samsung Hub
Singapore 049483

ISBN 978-1-5443-5183-4

Pagination has been changed from the original book for this custom publication. Therefore, cross-references will not be accurate.

Contents

RACE AND THE SOCIAL CONSTRUCTION OF DIFFERENCE

David Rae Morris / Polaris/Newscom

The city of New Orleans's decision to remove this statue of Robert E. Lee, and three others celebrating Confederate figures, led to protests, with some celebrating the removal and others claiming the move was disrespectful of the heritage of the South.

CHAPTER OUTLINE

LEARNING OBJECTIVES

LO 1.1   Explain how race and ethnicity are socially constructed.

LO 1.2   Evaluate the relationship between social contexts and race.

LO 1.3   Identify the concepts and operation of racism.

LO 1.4   Examine the link between our personal narratives and the broader "story" of race.

Our country has a history of memorializing wars and the people who fought them with medals, holidays, and monuments. The Civil War (1861–65) between the North and the South was quite possibly the bloodiest and subsequently the most commemorated four years in U.S. history. After the final shot was fired, some 1,500 memorials and monuments were created, including many commemorating the heroes of the Confederacy, the seven slaveholding Southern states that formally seceded from the Union in 1861 (Graham 2016). Over the past few years, protests around the appropriateness of these monuments have highlighted the racial fault lines in America.

In 2016, New Orleans, Louisiana, became a racial seismic epicenter as protests rocked the city. At issue was the city's decision to remove four landmark Civil War–related monuments: a statue of Jefferson Davis, president of the Confederacy;

statues of Confederate generals P. G. T. Beauregard and Robert E. Lee; and a monument memorializing a White supremacist uprising during the Reconstruction era.

As the city pondered how and what to rebuild after the devastation of Hurricane Katrina in 2005, anti-Confederate sentiment began to simmer. It reached a boiling point in June 2015 when nine Black churchgoers in Charleston, South Carolina, were killed by a gunman waving a Confederate flag (Wootson 2017). To many, these monuments represented not only the racially-based terrorism of groups like the Ku Klux Klan but also a sanitized history that "whitewashed" the Confederacy cause and glorified slavery and White supremacy (Landrieu 2017). After the monuments were successfully removed, under the cover of darkness and with snipers stationed nearby to protect the workers, lawmakers in Louisiana and Alabama immediately responded by passing laws to make it more difficult to remove Confederate monuments in the future (Park 2017).

Confederate monuments are a symptom of a much deeper set of issues that mark our nation's troubled history with race. The mayor of New Orleans, Mitch Landrieu (2017), remarked that we as a nation continue to confuse the "difference between remembrance of history and reverence of it." Our collective memories often reflect this same distortion as we attempt to reconcile our democratic principles of freedom, justice, and equality with the racial realities of prejudice, bigotry, and discrimination. Landrieu's statement and the controversy surrounding the removal of Confederate monuments mirror concerns that are deeply rooted within the social fabric of our country. They highlight the promises and the problems associated with race in the United States. What is race, and how has it become so central to our experiences? Is race so ingrained in our basic identities that it is now a permanent fixture of our social landscape? Alternatively, if race is a social invention, with a set of origins, purposes, and realities, then is it within our ability to influence, change, or eliminate it? The answers to these questions drive the purpose of this book.

■ THE SOCIAL CONSTRUCTION OF RACE

Nothing better demonstrates the complexity and social dynamics of race than performing an Internet image search using the term "biracial twins." When most children are born, they are assumed to belong to particular races because of the color of their skin. But race is not so simple. Even twins can have very different skin colors, and this can raise some interesting questions. Some twins who have one Black parent and one White parent are routinely asked to produce their birth certificates to prove that they are not only related but also twins. So are they White, or are they Black? It depends. In some cases, the twins self-identify according to their perceived racial identities (Perez 2015).

Defining Race

The term race refers to a social and cultural system by which we categorize people based on presumed biological differences. An examination of genetic patterns across the major world population groups reveals that while Africans have some genes unique to them as a group, all other groups share genetic patterns with Africans. This leads to the conclusion, held by most geneticists, anthropologists, and sociologists, that all humans are derived from Africans and that Africa is the cradle of humanity. Geneticists go further, declaring that the differences we observe between various groups are the results of geographical and social isolation, and that if such populations were to mix freely, then even these differences would disappear (Yudell, Roberts, DeSalle, and Tishkoff 2016).

Lucy and Maria Aylmer are twins, born to a half-Jamaican mother and a white father. Lucy identifies as white and Maria as black, despite their shared parentage.

AP Photo / Ken McKay

Since human genes have changed, or mutated, over time, we must question if race is either natural or static. If race were indeed a fact of nature, it would be simple to identify who falls into which racial category, and we would expect racial categories to remain static across history and societies. Differences in physical features, such as skin color, hair color, eye color, and height, exist both within and between groups. And as we've seen, physical features can vary even within families. However, these differences are not due to an underlying biological basis of race. There is more biological variation within our so-called racial groups than there is between them. Race must derive from human interventions. These interventions reflect the social construction of race.

Racial classifications have persisted as a means of advancing specific hierarchies through attention to the reputed differences in behaviors, skill sets, and inherent intelligence attributed to people according to their classifications. As a consequence, what social scientists and geneticists alike have come to understand is that race and racial categorizations are uniquely social creations that have been purposefully constructed. Specific rewards, privileges, and sanctions have been used to support and legitimate race. The systematic distribution of these rewards, privileges, and sanctions across populations through time has produced and reproduced social hierarchies that reflect our racial categorizations. We collectively refer to these systematic processes as the social construction of race.

Constructing Race around the World

If we examine the social construction of race across geographical spaces and historical periods, then an interesting range of constructions is immediately apparent.

South Africa

Many countries have historically instituted laws that dictated where the members of different racial groups could live and work, and how they must behave. Once such system, known as apartheid, existed in South Africa until 1994. One of the measures of determining race in South Africa was the so-called pencil test. If a pencil pushed through the hair stayed put, the person was deemed to have Afro-textured hair and might be classified as Black or Colored (of mixed racial heritage). If the pencil fell to the floor, the person was classified as White. A Colored classification allowed a person to have significantly more rights than those who were considered Black, but still fewer rights and responsibilities than those considered White. Given the multiple products and processes used to "straighten" Black hair, and the social benefits associated with enhanced social status, is it any wonder that many Black South Africans sought to have their identify changed to Colored? Apartheid allowed a racial hierarchy to be reified into law—an illustration of how race was socially constructed in South Africa. While technically illegal, these racial hierarchies are still a part of South African cultural identity and heritage, and the legacies of apartheid still haunt South Africa more than 20 years after the system officially ended.

South America

The Southern Cone of South America is a geographic region composed of the southernmost areas of the continent, including the countries of Argentina, Brazil, Chile, Paraguay, and Uruguay (see Figure 1.1). Among these Latin American countries, phenotypical traits—physical traits such as skin color, hair texture, and facial features typically used to characterize people into racial groups—are linked to socioeconomic status.

At the top of the hierarchy are White Hispanics and others with light skin. Mixed indigenous and African ancestry, often referred to as *mulatto,* is associated with less opportunity, higher levels of poverty, and lower social status. Those individuals who claim both indigenous and Hispanic ancestry, called *mestizos,* occupy a middle position and tend to have slightly more opportunities for social and economic advancement than do mulattos.

There are also nation-specific racial categorizations. The Brazilian census identifies six racial categories: *Brancos* (White), *Pardos* (Brown), *Pretos* (Black), *Amarelos* (East Asian), indigenous, and undeclared. Such categories and their links to the social and economic hierarchies in Latin American countries exist to this day in what scholars

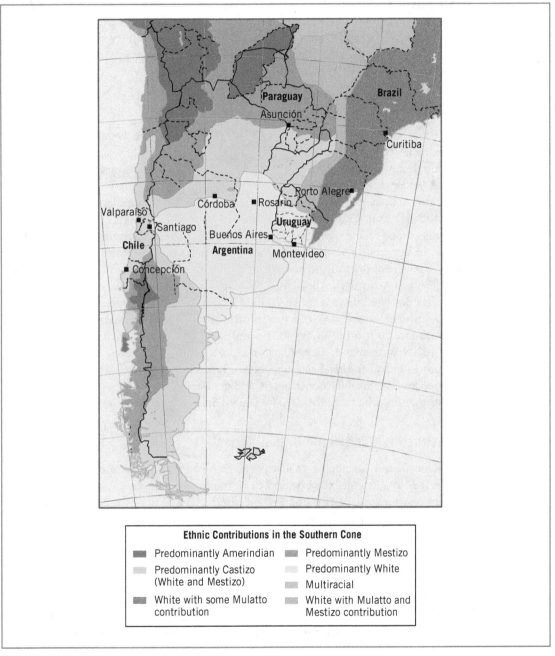

Ethnic Contributions in the Southern Cone

- Predominantly Amerindian
- Predominantly Castizo (White and Mestizo)
- White with some Mulatto contribution
- Predominantly Mestizo
- Predominantly White
- Multiracial
- White with Mulatto and Mestizo contribution

Source: Wikimedia Commons, https://commons.wikimedia.org/wiki/File:Southern_Cone_Ethnography.jpg.

refer to as pigmentocracies—governments and other social structures that grant political power based on a hierarchy defined by skin tone, regardless of race or social status (Telles and the Project on Ethnicity and Race in Latin America 2014). But these are not exclusive categorizations. One study conducted by the Brazilian Institute of Geography and Statistics, the governmental entity responsible for the census, asked people what racial categories they would place themselves in, and the researchers received 134 different answers (Fish 2011).

Australia

Race was similarly constructed in Australia when Britain began to colonize and marginalize the indigenous population in 1791. In the early phase of colonization, Britain declared much of Australia's most valuable land to be *terra nullius,* or "empty land." Under this determination, all of the natives, or Aboriginals, saw their rights to land revoked, as the Europeans declared the indigenous population's 50,000 years of residency null. Thus began an apartheid-like social structure, where Europeans were accorded all the rights, privileges, and status, while Aborigines were reduced to living in poverty on settlements. This segregated racial structure has been successfully challenged only in the last 20 years, as courts have begun to grant rights and privileges to Australia's Aborigines. The historical legacy of such a racialized structure has not been limited to Australia. Of note, several European nations used the declaration of *terra nullius* as a means of justifying colonial expansion and the subsequent racialization of indigenous peoples in many places, including, but not limited to, New Zealand, Grenada, Singapore, South Rhodesia, Tobago, Trinidad, Guano Islands, Burkina Faso, and Niger. In each case, a racial hierarchy favoring Europeans was socially constructed. Indigenous populations were subject to subjugation, isolation, or genocide. The United States is another one of these cases.

Constructing Race in the United States

Whiteness came into being as a way for European colonists to explain and justify imperialism, genocide, slavery, and exploitation. In Chapter 2, we will discuss the extent to which the construction of race in the United States follows the pattern of European settler colonialism and imperialism. For now, we present a brief explanation of how racial categorizations became significant within the United States.

The Significance of Where and When

The United States has its roots in three separate colonial settlements. These settlements, associated with the Spanish, French, and English, developed different types of racial classification structures. While all of them reserved the highest category for Europeans, they varied in how they accommodated other groups. This variability accounts for the slight differences we can still often observe between the former

Drawing by: H. Strickland Constable, 1899, Ireland from One or Two Neglected Points of View

IRISH IBERIAN   ANGLO-TEUTONIC   NEGRO

The Iberians are believed to have been originally an African race, who thousands of years ago spread themselves through Spain over Western Europe. Their remains are found in the barrows, or burying places, in sundry parts of these countries. The skulls are of low prognathous type. They came to Ireland, and mixed with the natives of the South and West, who themselves are supposed to have been of low type and descendants of savages of the Stone Age, who, in consequence of isolation from the rest of the world, had never been out-competed in the healthy struggle of life, and thus made way, according to the laws of nature, for superior races.

Constructing race in 1899. The caption that appeared with this image in an 1899 edition of *Harper's Weekly* reads: "The Iberians are believed to have been originally an African race, who thousands of years ago spread themselves through Spain over Western Europe. Their remains are found in the barrows, or burying places, in sundry parts of these countries. The skulls are of low prognathous type. They came to Ireland and mixed with the natives of the South and West, who themselves are supposed to have been of low type and descendants of savages of the Stone Age, who, in consequence of isolation from the rest of the world, had never been out-competed in the healthy struggle of life, and thus made way, according to the laws of nature, for superior races."

Spanish and French colonial regions (e.g., in California and Louisiana) and the former English colonial areas. These differences are most reflected in the heightened status of Creoles (people of mixed race, European and indigenous) in the former Spanish and French colonies and the more rigidly defined racial categories within the English. The reasons for these differences, as we will discover, are associated with the differences in settlement types. Here, it is important simply to note that these differences were real and that they further demonstrate the processes of the social construction of race.

The social construction of race also varies across time, as the sets of descriptors used to create racial categories have varied in different historical periods. At an earlier time in U.S. history, for example, the Irish were considered to be of African descent. The "Iberian hypothesis" purported that the "Black Irish" were descendants of Africans and those from the Gaelic island. Although the Iberian hypothesis has since been discredited (Radford 2015), in 1899 it was considered fact. Irish immigrants experienced a tremendous amount of prejudice in the United States and were not considered to be among the country's elite White ethnics. In Chapter 2 we shall see that these biases underscored many of our attitudes toward race and how Whiteness came into being.

In 1924, the Racial Integrity Act defined a "colored person" as anyone with any African or Native American ancestry at all; this is often referred to as the one-drop rule. The rules for defining who falls into what racial categories have long been inconsistent across the United States. Over time and in different states, the amount of ancestry required to make someone Black has variously been defined as one drop (of Black blood) and by fractions ranging from $\frac{1}{4}$ to $\frac{1}{8}$ to $\frac{1}{32}$. A person could "change" races by simply stepping over a state line. Why did having $\frac{1}{32}$ Black ancestry make someone Black, yet having $\frac{31}{32}$ of White ancestry not make someone White? And why have such clear-cut rules never been established for other racial groups? How many Asian ancestors are required to define someone as Asian? These inconsistencies exist because racial classifications are based not on biology but on social, political, and economic dynamics and power relationships. Under the one-drop rule, Native Americans of mixed ancestry were systematically classified as Negro (or Black) and denied tribal rights, and those who crossed the color line were subject to criminal punishments.

Race in the Contemporary United States

So what does this racially constructed system look like in the contemporary United States? Try this exercise: First, create a list of the racial groups in the United States. Then, write down your estimate of the percentage of the U.S. population that is accounted for by each group.

When we ask our students to attempt this exercise, the answers we get are varied. Some list four races; some list ten. Some include Hispanics/Latinos, and some do not. Some include Middle Easterners, while some do not. Some include a category for multiracial identity. Race is something we assume we all know when we see it, but we may in fact be "seeing" different things. Race cannot be reduced to physical features like skin color—in fact, while skin tone is often the first item we "check off" on our racial checklist, we then move to other social and visual clues.

The U.S. Constitution requires that a counting of the nation's population be conducted every 10 years—a national census (see Figure 1.2). The purposes and uses of the census have both changed and expanded across the years. The census was originally necessary to determine voting representation, including the numbers of representatives states could elect to Congress, the allocation of federal and state funds, and more. Over time, the census categories of race and other cultural and language groups have changed to reflect the nation's evolving population as well as, importantly, the political interests and power relations of the time.

So what have we discovered? Race is a social construction that artificially divides people into distinct groups based on characteristics such as physical appearance, ancestry, culture, ethnic classification, and the social, economic, and political needs, desires, and relations of a society at a given historical moment (Adams, Bell, and

Griffin 1997; Ferrante and Brown 2001). The U.S. Census Bureau, for instance, currently recognizes five racial categories, along with a "some other race" option (which was added in 2000 in response to public pressure). The five categories are as follows:

1. American Indian or Alaska Native
2. Asian
3. Black or African American
4. Native Hawaiian or other Pacific Islander
5. White

Not only have our official designations for race and ethnic groups differed over time, but how people identify themselves has also shown a great deal of variability. For example, from the 2000 census to that of 2010, almost 10 million U.S. residents changed how they identified their race when asked by the Census Bureau (Linshi 2014). This clearly demonstrates the fluidity of racial groups.

People often associate an elaborate array of behaviors, attitudes, and values with particular racial groups, presuming that these reflect innate or culturally specific traits. As one observer has noted: "What is called 'race' today is chiefly an outcome of intergroup struggles, marking the boundaries, and thus the identities, of 'us' and 'them' along with attendant ideas of social worth or stigma. As such, 'race' is an ideological construct that links supposedly innate traits of individuals to their place in the social order" (Rumbaut 2011).

We often assume that racial differences have existed throughout history, but race is a relatively new concept. Human differences exist along a continuum, and racial classifications have been arbitrarily imposed on that continuum, separating people into seemingly distinct groups, much as we separate the color spectrum into distinct categories that we have selected to label red, orange, yellow, green, and so on—though there is only one spectrum of color.

Recent genetic evidence presents a much more varied set of human identities. For example, most of us derive from multiple ancestries. Genomes reveal that the average African American can identify not only with African ancestry (about 73.2%) but also with European (24%) and Native American (0.8%). Latinos average about 18% Native American ancestry, 65% European ancestry (mostly from the Iberian Peninsula), and 6.2% African ancestry. And about 3.5% of European Americans carry African ancestry. These are more likely to be in southern states, such as South Carolina and Louisiana (where 12% of European Americans have at least 1% African ancestry). In Louisiana, about 8% of Europeans derive at least 1% of their ancestries from Native Americans (Wade 2014).

Figure 1.2 ■ Racial and Ethnic Categories Have Changed Over the Past 220 Years

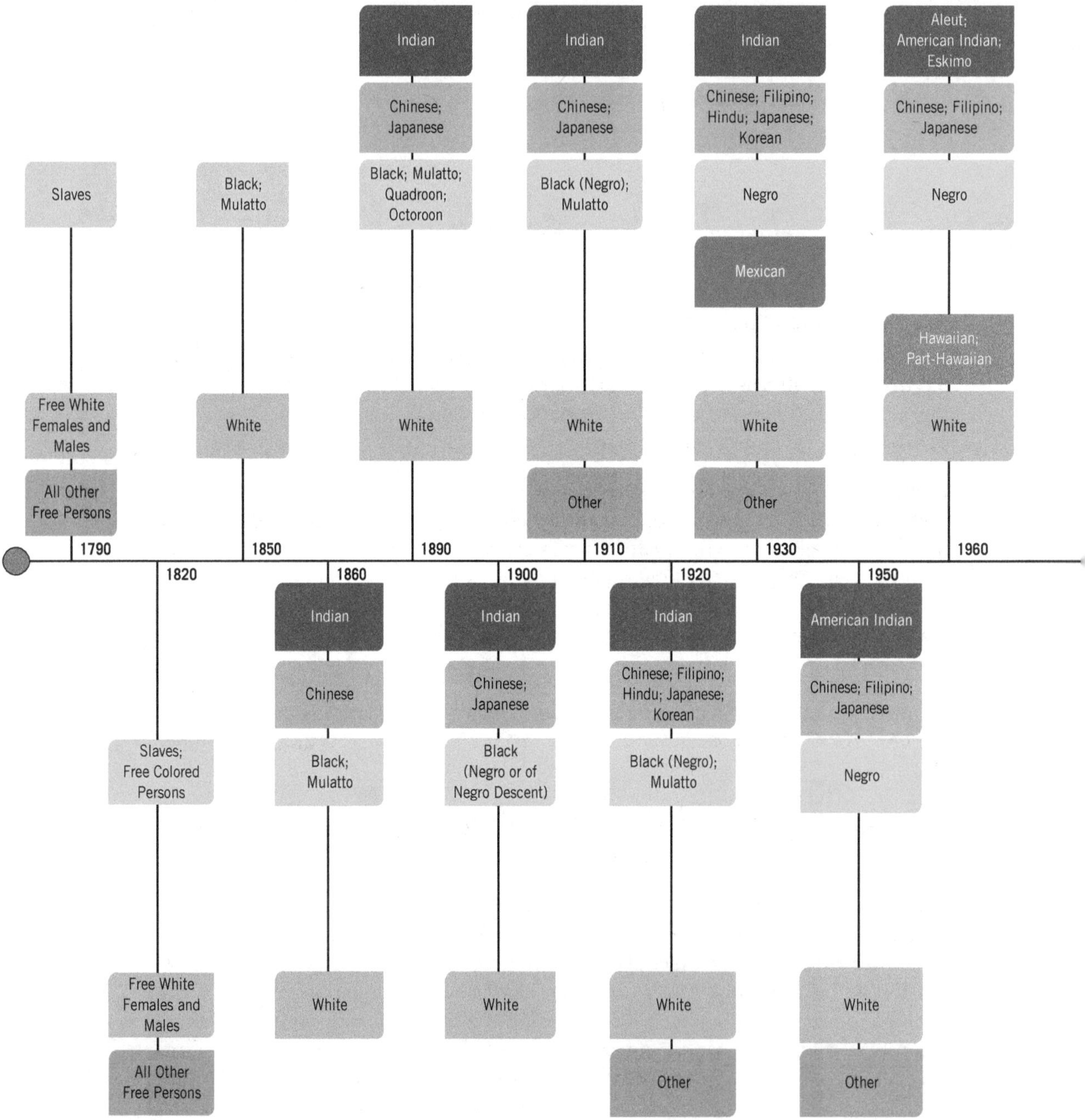

1790	1850	1890	1910	1930	1960
		Indian	Indian	Indian	Aleut; American Indian; Eskimo
		Chinese; Japanese	Chinese; Japanese	Chinese; Filipino; Hindu; Japanese; Korean	Chinese; Filipino; Japanese
Slaves	Black; Mulatto	Black; Mulatto; Quadroon; Octoroon	Black (Negro); Mulatto	Negro	Negro
				Mexican	
					Hawaiian; Part-Hawaiian
Free White Females and Males	White	White	White	White	White
All Other Free Persons			Other	Other	

1820	1860	1900	1920	1950
	Indian	Indian	Indian	American Indian
	Chinese	Chinese; Japanese	Chinese; Filipino; Hindu; Japanese; Korean	Chinese; Filipino; Japanese
Slaves; Free Colored Persons	Black; Mulatto	Black (Negro or of Negro Descent)	Black (Negro); Mulatto	Negro
Free White Females and Males	White	White	White	White
All Other Free Persons			Other	Other

Source: U.S. Census Bureau, "Measuring Race and Ethnicity across the Decades: 1790–2010," http://www.census.gov/population/race/data/MREAD_1790_2010.html.

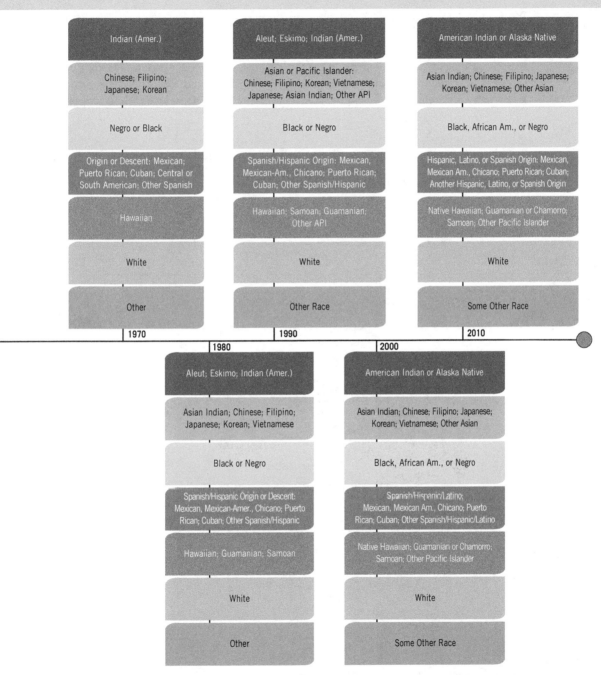

1970

- Indian (Amer.)
- Chinese; Filipino; Japanese; Korean
- Negro or Black
- Origin or Descent: Mexican; Puerto Rican; Cuban; Central or South American; Other Spanish
- Hawaiian
- White
- Other

1980

- Aleut; Eskimo; Indian (Amer.)
- Asian Indian; Chinese; Filipino; Japanese; Korean; Vietnamese
- Black or Negro
- Spanish/Hispanic Origin or Descent: Mexican, Mexican-Amer., Chicano; Puerto Rican; Cuban; Other Spanish/Hispanic
- Hawaiian; Guamanian; Samoan
- White
- Other

1990

- Aleut; Eskimo; Indian (Amer.)
- Asian or Pacific Islander: Chinese; Filipino; Korean; Vietnamese; Japanese; Asian Indian; Other API
- Black or Negro
- Spanish/Hispanic Origin: Mexican, Mexican-Am., Chicano; Puerto Rican; Cuban; Other Spanish/Hispanic
- Hawaiian; Samoan; Guamanian; Other API
- White
- Other Race

2000

- American Indian or Alaska Native
- Asian Indian; Chinese; Filipino; Japanese; Korean; Vietnamese; Other Asian
- Black, African Am., or Negro
- Spanish/Hispanic/Latino; Mexican, Mexican Am., Chicano; Puerto Rican; Cuban; Other Spanish/Hispanic/Latino
- Native Hawaiian; Guamanian or Chamorro; Samoan; Other Pacific Islander
- White
- Some Other Race

2010

- American Indian or Alaska Native
- Asian Indian; Chinese; Filipino; Japanese; Korean; Vietnamese; Other Asian
- Black, African Am., or Negro
- Hispanic, Latino, or Spanish Origin: Mexican, Mexican Am., Chicano; Puerto Rican; Cuban; Another Hispanic, Latino, or Spanish Origin
- Native Hawaiian; Guamanian or Chamorro; Samoan; Other Pacific Islander
- White
- Some Other Race

Note: According to the 2000 Census, as the 2010 Census did not ask questions about ancestry. Please note that respondents may have selected more than one ancestry group.

The Role of Ethnicity

While race has been imposed on physical bodies, ethnicity encompasses cultural aspects of individuals' lives, including religion, tradition, language, ancestry, nation, geography, history, beliefs, and practice. Ethnic groups often see themselves, and are seen by others, as having distinct cultural identities. Physical characteristics are not usually tied to definitions of ethnicity. For example, Blacks in the United States come from many different ethnic backgrounds, including African Americans whose ancestors arrived enslaved generations ago and recent immigrants from Ethiopia, Jamaica, and other parts of the world. Often we confuse ancestry with ethnicity and race. The term ancestry typically refers to point of origin, lineage, or descent. For instance, Abby, one of the authors of this text, is racially White, ethnically Jewish, and of Eastern European ancestry. Ancestry is often one characteristic in definitions of ethnicity or race (see Figure 1.3).

Figure 1.3 ■ The Nine Largest Ancestry Groups in The United States

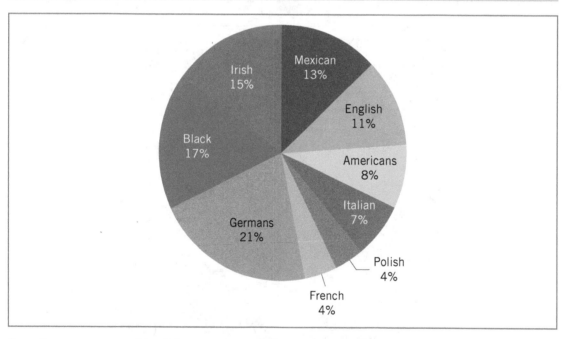

Source: Derived from data in Liz O'Connor, Gus Lubin, and Dina Spector, "The Largest Ancestry Groups in the United States," Business Insider, August 13, 2013, http://www.businessinsider.com/largest-ethnic-groups-in-america-2013-8.

Often when we concentrate on large racial groups in the United States, we tend to ignore just how diverse we are as a nation. Although the most recent census, in 2010, did not ask a question regarding ancestry, the Census Bureau's American Community Survey tracks most major ancestry groups on an ongoing basis. The data collected by that survey reveal that Germans and Blacks make up the largest single ancestry groups within the United States.

When we focus on racial groups as distinct groups whose members supposedly have much in common while ignoring the ethnic and ancestral diversity within the socially constructed categories, we further exaggerate the significance of racial designations. Furthermore, we erase the differences among the various and diverse ethnic peoples grouped into these racial categories. The only thing that people grouped together under a racial designation share is a history of oppression based on their racialization. Other than that, racial categories themselves tell us very little about the people classified into them.

Native Americans

The original, indigenous inhabitants of the Americas, Native Americans (or American Indians) and Alaska Natives, do not constitute one single race. As of the 2010 census, members of these groups made up 2% of the total U.S. population. Of these, about 49% exclusively defined themselves as either American Indians or Alaska Natives. The remaining 51% identified as some combination of American Indian or Alaska Native and one or more other races (U.S. Census Bureau 2012). A total of 630 separate federally recognized American Indian and Alaska Native reservations existed in 2012, excluding the Hawaiian Home Lands. There are 566 federally recognized American Indian and Alaska Native tribes, with the five largest tribal groupings being the Cherokee, Navajo, Choctaw, Mexican American Indian, and Chippewa groupings (see Figure 1.4). At the time of the 2010 census, the majority of Native Americans were living in 10 states: California, Oklahoma, Arizona, Texas, New York, New Mexico, Washington, North Carolina, Florida, and Michigan (U.S. Census Bureau 2012).

Asian Americans

All racial categories can be described as "panethnic." Yen Le Espiritu coined the term panethnicity in 1992 in reference to Asian Americans (see Espiritu 1994). It is generally applied to regional groups who are placed into a large category. As Espiritu points out, many Asian groups—including Chinese, Hmong, Japanese, Korean, Bangladeshi, Asian Indian, and Vietnamese—have been lumped together and viewed as an artificial whole.

Asians make up 5.8% of the total U.S. population. While many Americans are aware of the increasing presence of Hispanic-origin immigrants, Asians actually now make up an even larger share of immigrants to the United States. In 2014, the Asian share of the U.S. foreign-born population increased to 30% of the nation's 42.4 million immigrants (Zong and Batalova 2014). In that year, most of the 4.2 million Asians entering the United States came from Southeast Asia, followed by East Asia, South Central Asia, and Western Asia. India and China accounted for the largest share of these immigrants (17% each), followed by the Philippines (15%), Vietnam (10%), and Korea (9%). Asian immigrants also come from dozens of other countries in the Far East, Southeast Asia, and the Indian continent (Zong and Batalova 2016).

Figure 1.4 ■ American Indians and Alaskan Natives Identify Across Different Tribal Groupings

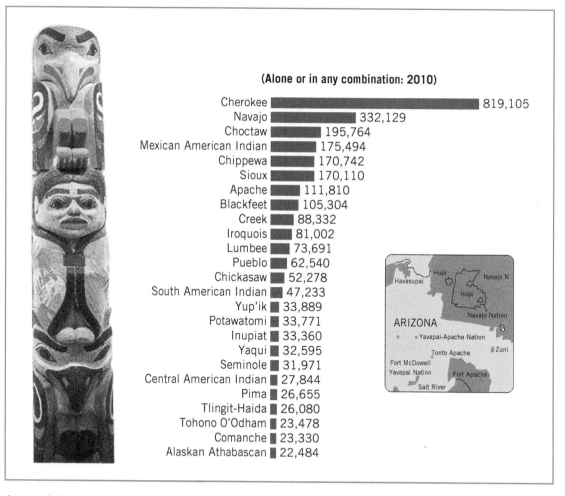

(Alone or in any combination: 2010)

Tribal Grouping	Population
Cherokee	819,105
Navajo	332,129
Choctaw	195,764
Mexican American Indian	175,494
Chippewa	170,742
Sioux	170,110
Apache	111,810
Blackfeet	105,304
Creek	88,332
Iroquois	81,002
Lumbee	73,691
Pueblo	62,540
Chickasaw	52,278
South American Indian	47,233
Yup'ik	33,889
Potawatomi	33,771
Inupiat	33,360
Yaqui	32,595
Seminole	31,971
Central American Indian	27,844
Pima	26,655
Tlingit-Haida	26,080
Tohono O'Odham	23,478
Comanche	23,330
Alaskan Athabascan	22,484

Source: U.S. Census Bureau, "25 Largest Tribal Groupings among American Indians and Alaska Natives," 2010, https://www.census.gov/content/dam/Census/newsroom/facts-for-features/2014/cb14-ff26_aian_graphic.jpg.

Black Americans

Historically, scholars have rarely discussed ethnicity among Blacks. This further highlights racial designations while marginalizing the differences among various ethnic groups. Some Blacks in the United States can trace their roots back to slavery, while others are recent immigrants from Africa. People defined as Black may have African, Caribbean, Haitian, Filipino, and other diverse ancestries. In fact, racial designations based on geography become meaningless as we attempt to apply them to North Africans, such as Egyptians, Moroccans, and Algerians (groups frequently defined by the U.S. Census Bureau as White). According to the U.S. Census Bureau (2015), in 2014 Blacks constituted an estimated 13% of the U.S. population.

As of 2015, 2.1 million African immigrants were living in the United States, accounting for 4.8% of the U.S. population, compared to just 0.8% in 1970. While typically these immigrants are lumped into the racial category of Black, Figure 1.5 shows that such racial homogenization hides much of the ethnic diversity among them (Anderson 2017).

White Ethnic Groups

White ethnics, who have until recently provided the largest share of immigration to these shores, derive mostly from European countries. Many of these today simply refer to themselves as "American." In fact, major streams of European immigration can be identified during the colonial era, the first portion of the 19th century, and the period from the 1880s to 1920. European immigrants were granted increased access to the United States as stipulated in the 1882 Chinese Exclusion Act. This quota system was not effectively ended until the passage of the Immigration and Nationality Act of 1965. White ethnic groups include people of British, Greek, Russian, German, and Norwegian ancestry, as well as many others. Figure 1.6 shows that European immigration has been relatively stable over the past 20 years. In 2010, the top five countries of origin for European immigrants were the United Kingdom (670,000, or 14%), Germany (605,000, or 13%), Poland (476,000, or 10%), Russia (383,000, or 8%), and Italy (365,000, or 8%) (Russell and Batalova 2012).

Hispanics

If an individual identifies with an ethnic group that speaks Spanish, then the U.S. Census Bureau labels that person as Hispanic. Hispanics may have families that came to the United States from Spain, Mexico, Guatemala, Cuba, or one of many other Spanish-speaking countries (see Figure 1.7). They may be White, Black, or some other race. Other than language, they may have nothing in common. Hispanic is a category created by the government, and many people classified as Hispanic prefer to define themselves as Latino/a, Chicano/a, or Mexican American, Cuban

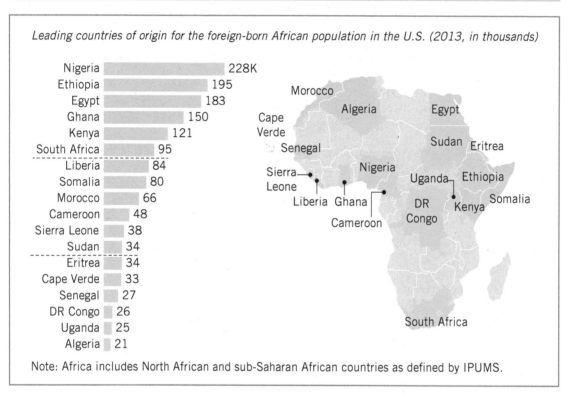

Leading countries of origin for the foreign-born African population in the U.S. (2013, in thousands)

Nigeria	228K
Ethiopia	195
Egypt	183
Ghana	150
Kenya	121
South Africa	95
Liberia	84
Somalia	80
Morocco	66
Cameroon	48
Sierra Leone	38
Sudan	34
Eritrea	34
Cape Verde	33
Senegal	27
DR Congo	26
Uganda	25
Algeria	21

Note: Africa includes North African and sub-Saharan African countries as defined by IPUMS.

Source: Chart and Map: "Nigeria, Ethiopia, Egypt are top birthplaces for African immigrants in the U.S." From African immigrant population in U.S. steadily climbs by Monica Anderson, Pew Research Center Fact Tank, February 14, 2017.

American, or the like. Some sociologists argue that Latino/as have been historically racialized and defined as inferior by Whites and should be classified as a race rather than an ethnic group. Much of the rich contemporary literature on racial inequality in the United States adopts this definition of Hispanics/Latino/as as a racialized group (Feagin and Cobas 2013; Ortiz and Telles 2012). We also generally treat them as a racial group in this book, and, indeed, many Hispanics have recently organized to push for categorization as a racial group in the next census, in 2020. Throughout this text, we will frequently use the terminology adopted by the research under discussion, thus referring at times to Hispanics and at other times to Latino/as (also, at times we will refer to Blacks and at other times to African Americans).

Figure 1.6 ■ European Immigration to the United States Has Been Steady Over the Past Twenty Years

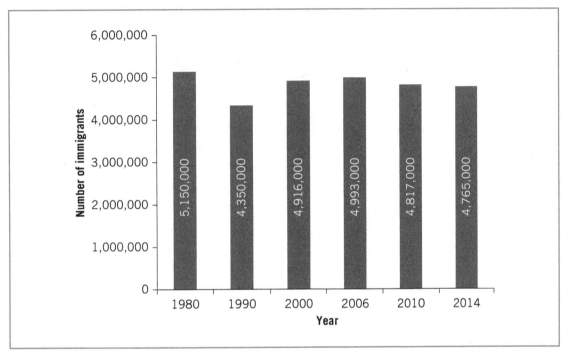

Source: Jie Zong and Jeanne Batalova, "European Immigrants in the United States," Migration Policy Institute, December 1, 2015, http://www.migrationpolicy.org/article/european-immigrants-united-states. Data from U.S. Census Bureau, American Community Surveys, 2006, 2010, and 2014; and Campbell J. Gibson and Kay Jung, "Historical Census Statistics on the Foreign-Born Population of the United States: 1850–2000," Working Paper 81, U.S. Census Bureau, February 2006.

Although it is surprising to many, the U.S. Census Bureau does not currently list Hispanic as a race, instead defining Hispanics as an ethnic group. The census includes a separate question specifically about Hispanic origin, asking self-identified Hispanics to select Mexican, Puerto Rican, Cuban, or other. The census form then asks them to identify their race.

Racial and Ethnic Compositions in the Future

So what will our country look like in the next 50 years? Projections of population growth indicate that minorities (including Hispanics, Blacks, Asian Americans, and Native Hawaiians and other Pacific Islanders) will make up slightly more than 50%

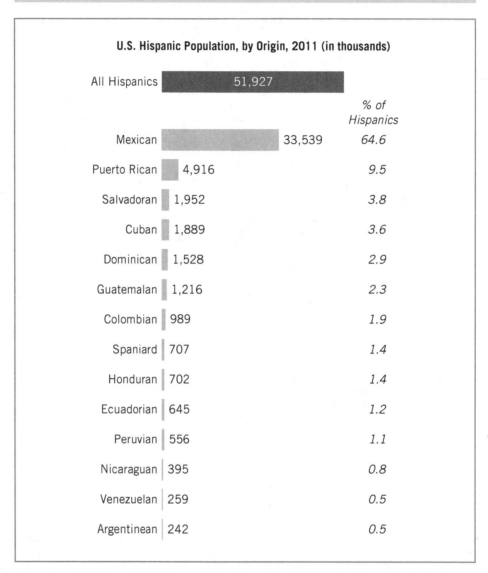

U.S. Hispanic Population, by Origin, 2011 (in thousands)

		% of Hispanics
All Hispanics	51,927	
Mexican	33,539	64.6
Puerto Rican	4,916	9.5
Salvadoran	1,952	3.8
Cuban	1,889	3.6
Dominican	1,528	2.9
Guatemalan	1,216	2.3
Colombian	989	1.9
Spaniard	707	1.4
Honduran	702	1.4
Ecuadorian	645	1.2
Peruvian	556	1.1
Nicaraguan	395	0.8
Venezuelan	259	0.5
Argentinean	242	0.5

Source: Figure 2, "U.S. Hispanic Origin Groups, by Population, 2013. In The Impact of Slowing Immigration: Foreign-Born Share Falls Among 14 Largest U.S. Hispanic Origin Groups, by Gustavo Lopez and Eileen Patten, Pew Research Center Hispanic Trends, September 15, 2015.

of the U.S. population. The most significant changes will be seen in the reduced numbers of Whites and the almost doubling of the numbers of Hispanics and other minorities. We often read headlines predicting that Whites will become a minority. However, these are misleading. Whites will still be the single largest group in the United States, constituting 49.4% of the population in 2060 (Figure 1.8). The United States will become a minority-majority nation, which means that the total of all minority groups combined will make up the majority of the population. We may see little change in the dynamics of power and race relations, however, as the proportion of Whites will still be nearly twice that of any individual minority group.

Figure 1.8 ■ Population Growth Projections Over the Next Fifty Years Predict a Minority-Majority Nation

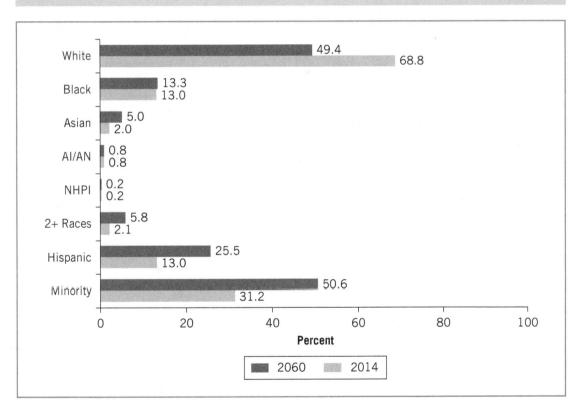

Source: U.S. Census Bureau, "Projections of the Size and Composition of the U.S. Population: 2014–2060," Population Estimates and Projections, Current Population Reports, March 2015.

CRITICAL THINKING

1. History has shown that race and ethnicity are socially constructed. What do current trends suggest about how these social constructions may change in the future?

2. How might these changes affect social institutions such as marriage and family, education, and the military?

3. In what ways might these changes affect how we, as Americans, view ourselves? How might this affect how individuals categorize others and how they self-identify?

4. Can you trace your roots? What different racial and ethnic groups are in your family tree? What does this say about how we define racial and ethnic groups?

■ THE SOCIAL MATRIX OF RACE

Our goal in this book is to provide you with historical perspectives, theoretical frameworks, and diverse views of race and racial ideologies so that you can intelligently participate and contribute to such dialogues. We will offer you a variety of ways in which you can understand your identity, your environments, the relationships between those, and the ways you can change yourself and your society with dignity and self-determination. We focus particularly on race and the way it shapes our identities, society and its institutions, and prospects for change. But we also examine race within the context of gender, class, and other social identities that interact with one another and reflect the way we live as social beings.

A number of scholars have embraced the image of racial identity as a matrix (Case 2013; Collins 2000; Ferber, Jiménez, O'Reilly Herrera, and Samuels 2009). Generally, a matrix is the surrounding environment in which something (e.g., values, cells, humans) originates, develops, and grows. The concept of a matrix captures the basic sociological understanding that contexts—social, cultural, economic, historical, and otherwise—matter. Figure 1.9 is our visual representation of the social matrix of race, depicting the intersecting worlds of identity, social institutions, and cultural and historical contexts, connecting with one another on the micro and macro levels.

If our primary focus were gender, we could center the gendered self in such a matrix. In this text we center the concepts and experiences of race within the context of our many shifting social identities and systems of inequality. Our social identities are the ways in which our group memberships, in such things as races, classes, and genders,

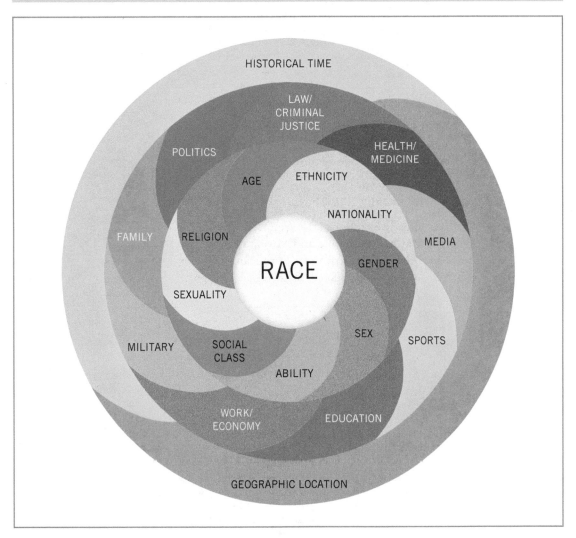

Source: Copyright Rodney D. Coates, Abby L. Ferber, and David L. Brunsma.

help define our sense of self. While we often assume a concrete or single group identity, the reality is that identity is seldom so simple. For example, while many of us identify as being White, Black, Hispanic, Asian, or Native American, few of us are racially or ethnically homogeneous. Consequently, how we derive our racial identity is actually a result of both historical and contemporary social constructions.

The same can be said regarding our social status, class, gender, and other identities. We also recognize that these identities interact in ways that produce extremely nuanced and complex, dynamic identities. The third ring of the social matrix of race consists of the social institutions in which we live and interact. Social institutions are patterned and structured sets of roles and behaviors centered on the performance of important social tasks within any given society. These institutions help order and facilitate social interactions. That being so, many of our activities happen within social institutions such as marriage and family, education, sports, the military, and the economy. In Figure 1.9 we have included only the social institutions we examine in this text; this is not an exhaustive list. Finally, all of these systems are shaped by place and time.

To support an understanding of race within the context of a social matrix, in the following sections we introduce the five key insights about race that we will develop throughout this text (see Table 1.1).

Race Is Inherently Social

We have already introduced the argument that race is a social construction. As race theorists Matthew Desmond and Mustafa Emirbayer (2010, 51) put it, "You do not come into this world African or European or Asian; rather, this world comes into you." If races are constructed, it makes sense then to ask: When does this happen,

Table 1.1 ■ Five Key Insights about Race	
Race is inherently social.	Race has no biological basis, and it varies both cross-culturally and historically.
Race is a narrative.	We learn narrative story lines that we draw upon to interpret what we see and experience, and these stories become embedded in our minds as truth, closing off other ways of seeing and sense making.
Racial identity is relational and intersectional.	Our racial identity is defined in our relationships to others, based on interactions with them and our reactions to our experiences and socialization. Further, our racial identity is shaped by, and experienced in the context of, our other social identities, such as gender, class, sexuality, ability, and age.
Race is institutional and structural.	Independently and together, various institutional structures, including family, school, community, and religion, influence our actions and beliefs about race.
We are active agents in the matrix.	We move among a variety of social institutions, and as we do, we contribute to their reproduction. We make choices every day, often unconsciously, that either maintain or subvert racial power dynamics and inequality.

and why? The creation of "races" occurred at a specific point in time to advance specific relations of inequality. The classifications were invented by those they were created to serve, not by those who came to be defined as "Others" by Whites. We will examine this history in Chapter 2.

Race Is a Narrative

As we have established, race is not real; it is a fiction with very real consequences. Because it is fictional, scholars across many disciplines have used the language of storytelling to discuss race. For example, perhaps one of the most dominant stories we hear today is that race is a taboo topic. When children ask their parents about racial differences, they are often hushed and told not to talk about such things in public. Perhaps the most significant racial narrative is the story that races exist in nature. We have just shown that this is not true. Yet until we are taught otherwise, most of us go through life assuming that biological racial differences exist. This is the power of narrative in our lives as social beings.

Anthropologist Audrey Smedley (2007) has identified some of the key features of this narrative. In it, racial classifications are constructed as follows:

1. They are exclusive, discrete classifications.

2. They involve visible physical differences that reflect inherent internal ones (such as intelligence, disposition, morals).

3. They are inherited.

4. They are unchanging, determined by nature and/or God.

5. They are valued differently and ranked hierarchically (in terms of superiority, beauty, degree of civilization, capacity for moral reasoning, and more).

This narrative makes clear that the ideology of race privileges some groups by dividing people into artificial, hierarchical categories to justify inequitable access to resources.

The ideology of race is part of what Joe Feagin (2010) identifies as the "white racial frame." In societies characterized by racial hierarchies, racial frames are constructed from the ideological justifications, processes, procedures, and institutions that define and structure society. They are the "comprehensive orienting structure or tool kit by which dominant racial groups and others are understood," and their actions are interpreted within social settings (Feagin 2010, 13). According to Feagin (2010, 10–11), a racial frame consists of the following:

1. racial stereotypes (a beliefs aspect);

2. racial narratives and interpretations (integrating cognitive aspects);

3. racial images (a visual aspect) and language accents (an auditory aspect);

4. racialized emotions (a "feelings" aspect); and

5. inclinations to discriminatory action.

The repetition of the White racial frame over generations, in fact since the founding of the United States, is the key to its power. When the same messages are repeated over and over, they appear to be part of our social being; they become "natural" to us.

In her popular book *Storytelling for Social Justice* (2010), educator and activist Lee Anne Bell provides a model for analyzing stories about race. She argues that there are essentially four different kinds of stories that we encounter in our lives: stock stories, concealed stories, resistance stories, and transforming stories.

- *Stock stories:* "Stock stories are the tales told by the dominant group," but they are often embraced by those whose oppression they reinforce (Bell 2010, 23). They inform and organize the practices of social institutions and are encoded in law, public policy, public space, history, and culture. Stock stories are shaped by the White racial frame.

- *Concealed stories:* We can always find concealed stories if we look closely enough. These consist of the data and voices that stock stories ignore and often convey a very different understanding of identity and inequity. In the case of concealed stories, "we explore such questions as: What are the stories about race and racism that we don't hear? Why don't we hear them? How are such stories lost/left out? How do we recover these stories? What do these stories show us about racism that stock stories do not?" (24).

- *Resistance stories:* Narratives that directly challenge stock stories are resistance stories. They speak of defying domination and actively struggling for racial justice and social change. "Guiding questions for discovering/uncovering resistance stories include: What stories exist (historical or contemporary) that serve as examples of resistance? What role does resistance play in challenging the stock stories about racism? What can we learn about antiracist action and perseverance against the odds by looking at these stories?" (25).

- *Transforming stories:* Once we examine concealed and resistance stories, we can use them to write transforming stories that guide our actions as we work toward a more just society. "Guiding questions include: What would it look like if we transformed the stock stories? What can we draw from resistance stories to create new stories about what ought to be? What kinds of stories can support our ability to speak out and act where instances of racism occur?" (26).

Many people claim color blindness in regard to race and ethnicity—that is, they assert that they do not see race or ethnicity, only humans—and the idea of color blindness informs many of our most prevalent stock stories today. According to this ideology, if we were all to embrace a color-blind attitude and just stop "seeing" race, race and its issues would finally become relics of the past. This approach argues that we should treat people simply as human beings, rather than as racialized beings (Plaut 2010). In fact, White people in the United States generally believe that "we have achieved racial equality," and about half believe that African Americans are doing as well as, or even better than, Whites (Bush 2011, 4). But pretending race does not exist is not the same as creating equality.

Just when the blatantly discriminatory policies and practices of Jim Crow racism, the laws and practices that originated in the American South to enforce racial segregation, were finally crumbling under attack, the early foundations of a "new racism" were taking form (Irons 2010). This new racism is much less overt, avoiding the use of blatantly racist terminology. Sociologist Eduardo Bonilla-Silva (2010) has labeled this ideology color-blind racism. According to Bonilla-Silva, color-blind ideology has four components:

- *Abstract liberalism:* Abstract concepts of equal opportunity, rationality, free choice, and individualism are used to argue that discrimination is no longer a problem, and any individual who works hard can succeed.

- *Naturalization:* Ongoing inequality is reframed as the result of natural processes rather than social relations. Segregation is explained, for example, as the result of people's natural inclination to live near others of the same race.

- *Cultural racism:* It is claimed that inherent cultural differences serve to separate racialized groups.

- *Minimization of racism:* It is argued that we now have a fairly level playing field, everyone has equal opportunities to succeed, and racism is no longer a real problem.

Saul Loeb / AFP / Getty Images

Color-blind ideology leads to the conclusion that we've done all we can in regard to racial inequality. Many Whites invoke the election of Barack Obama to the presidency as confirmation of their assumptions of a color-blind nation (Bonilla-Silva 2010; Cunnigen and Bruce 2010). The concealed story revealed by sociology, however, is that racial inequality has been and remains entrenched in the United States.

While many embrace color blindness as nonracist, by ignoring the extent to which race still shapes people's life chances and opportunities, this view actually reinforces and reproduces the subtle and institutional racial inequality that shapes our lives. Throughout this text, we will examine the extent to which racial inequality is still pervasive, as well as many stock stories in circulation today that make it difficult for us to see this reality. We will challenge many stock stories by exploring concealed and resistance stories, and by considering the possibilities for constructing transformative stories.

Racial Identity Is Relational and Intersectional

As philosopher Elizabeth Spelman (1988) points out, we often think about our various identities—race, gender, sexuality, class, ability—as though they are connected like the beads of a necklace. But unlike the beads of the necklace, our separate identities can't just be popped apart. They intersect and shape each other; they are relational and intersectional (Crenshaw 1991).

The relational aspects of race are demonstrated by the fact that categories of race are often defined in opposition to each other (for example, to be White means one is not Black, Asian, Hispanic, or Native American) and according to where they fall along the continuum of hierarchy. Race is also relational in its intersections with other social identities, such as gender and class.

Intersectional theories argue that race, gender, and other salient social identities are intertwined and inseparable, and cannot be comprehended on their own. Sociologist Ivy Ken offers a useful metaphor. If we think about race as sugar, gender as flour, and class as baking soda, what happens when we mix them and a few other ingredients together? If we are lucky, we end up with cookies; we "produce something new—something that would not exist if that mixing had not occurred" (Ken 2008, 156). When these ingredients are combined, they are changed in the process.

David J. Connor (2006), a special education teacher in New York City, provides an example. He wondered why his classes were filled overwhelmingly with African American and Latino males despite the fact that learning disabilities occur in both males and females across class and race. Connor found that he needed an intersectional perspective to understand: "I noticed that the label [learning disabled] signified different outcomes for different people. What seemed to be a beneficial category of disability to middle-class, white students, by triggering various supports and services—served to disadvantage black and/or Latino/a urban youngsters, who were more likely to be placed in restrictive, segregated settings" (154). Here, race, class, and gender intersect to produce different consequences for differently situated youth.

As this example demonstrates, sources of oppression are related, and interrelated, in varied ways. There is no single formula for understanding how they work together. We are all shaped by all of these significant constructs, whether they privilege us or contribute to our oppression; we all experience specific configurations of race, class, and gender that affect our subjectivities, opportunities, and life chances.

Although its name is new, intersectional theory has a long history. Early theorists like Maria Stewart, Sojourner Truth, Frederick Douglass, Ida B. Wells, and Anna

Julia Cooper struggled with the ways race divided the women's suffrage movement, and gender limited Black women's participation in the antislavery movement. Decades later, women of color waged battles for full inclusion within the civil rights and women's movements. African American sociologists like Belinda Robnett (1999) and Bernice McNair Barnett (1995) have examined the ways in which the foundational leadership activities of Black women in many civil rights organizations have been ignored or written out of history (becoming concealed stories). Vicki Ruiz (1999) has examined similar dynamics in her research on the work of Chicanas in the Chicano movement. We can find many resistance stories in the lives of women of color who have refused to direct their energies toward just one form of oppression, arguing that their lives are shaped by their race and their gender simultaneously.

An intersectional approach does not require that we always examine every form of inequality. Instead, we need to recognize that intersectionality permeates every subject we study, and that even when we choose to focus on a single system of inequality, such as race, we must bring an intersectional lens to the work or we will never get a full picture of the experiences and dynamics of race.

Over the past few decades, research involving explicitly intersectional analysis has accelerated. Sociologists and others have examined the ways our various social locations intersect and interact in shaping our lives and society at every level. These represent interconnected axes of oppression and privilege that shape all of our lived experiences (Collins 2000).

Race Is Institutional and Structural

To say that race is institutional is to recognize that it operates alongside and in tandem with our dominant social institutions. For instance, education is a social institution in which there are roles (e.g., teachers and students) and expected behaviors (e.g., teaching and learning) that come together as a social structure to educate. But schools also contribute to other important social tasks, including socialization and social control (Spade and Ballantine 2011).

From the perspective of an individual in a human community, we might think about an institution by completing the following statement: "In this society/community, there is a *way* to do [fill in the blank]." In a society, like the United States, there is a *way* to do marriage, for example. When we mention the word *marriage* we are invoking a cultural script as well as a social structure—certain bodies come to mind, certain expectations, certain relationships, certain beginnings and outcomes. This is, perhaps, why gaining the right to marry has been such an amazing uphill battle for same-sex couples—as "same-sex marriage" runs counter to the prevailing sense of the institution of "marriage" (Baunach 2012). All of our dominant social institutions organize our lives, and they do so in deeply powerful ways that are intimately tied to how race (as well as gender, class, and sexuality) fundamentally structures and organizes our lives within society.

We Are Active Agents in the Matrix

While constructs of race and ethnicity shape us, we also shape them. Stories are often simply internalized, processed and made sense of by individuals and groups. Human beings, as active agents, have the potential to question inherited stories. Throughout this text we will examine various kinds of stories so that each of us may be better educated and informed in order to develop and support the stories by which we want to live our lives. It is only in this way that we can contribute to the construction of transformative stories that might produce a more equitable society.

Once we realize that race is socially constructed, it follows that we recognize our role as active agents in reconstructing it—through our actions and through the stories we construct that inform our actions (Markus and Moya 2010, 4). Emphasizing the concept of agency is also essential to creating social change. If race is something we *do,* then we can begin to do it differently. Yet many people believe that race is biological, and so they believe it is inevitable. If people believe that they can make changes, then they inherently understand the complex factors that shape their own possibilities (Bush 2011). Such agency empowers people to resist and transform the economic, political, and social realities associated with racial frames and other forms of inequality.

It is because we, too, embrace the concept of agency that we have written this text. We hope to make visible the stock stories that perpetuate racial inequality, and to examine the ways in which those narratives govern the operations of organizations and institutions. All of us, as individuals, play a role in reproducing or subverting the dominant narratives, whether we choose to or not. While we inherit stories about race that help us to explain the world around us, we can also seek out alternative stories. All of us, as individuals, play a role in the reproduction of institutional structures, from our workplaces to our places of worship to our schools and our homes.

Each of the key insights that inform our framework, discussed above, is essential. Each provides just one piece of the puzzle. Further, these elements interact and work together, constantly influencing one another from moment to moment, so that it is often difficult to look at any one piece in isolation. Racial attitudes and racialized social structures need to be examined in relationship to one another. For example, many scholars have argued that economic insecurity and resource scarcity often fan the flames of race prejudice. Critical knowledge is gained when we understand how dominant discourses and ideology preserve and perpetuate the status quo. Understanding how these dominant discourses are framed and how they are buttressed by our institutional practices, policies, and mechanisms allows us to see not only how these patterns are replicated and reproduced but also how they can be replaced (Bush 2011, 37).

CRITICAL THINKING

1. If race is a social construction, how might different institutions affect how race is perceived? How might these perceptions vary across time and place?

2. Using yourself as an example, how has your identity changed as you shifted from being a preteen to a teen to a college student? Do these changes remain constant across different institutions? (Think about the various clubs, committees, and groups to which you belong.)

3. What kinds of impacts can you have in the various groups to which you belong? In what ways do your possible impacts reflect your various identities?

4. Are there some groups to which you have greater or lesser access? What does your degree of access suggest about your level of agency?

■ THE OPERATION OF RACISM

In the first half of this chapter, we have examined what race is, how it is constructed, and how it is reproduced. We now shift our focus to the concept and operation of racism.

Prejudice and Discrimination

Anyone can be the victim of prejudice. Prejudice is a judgment of an individual or group, often based on race, ethnicity, religion, gender, class, or other social identities. It is often shaped by, and also leads to, the promotion of stereotypes, which are assumptions or generalizations applied to an entire group. Even seemingly positive stereotypes put people in boxes, like the myth of Asian Americans as the "model minority," which includes the stereotype that all Asian Americans are gifted in math and science. How might this stereotype affect Asian American students who are not doing well in school? How does it prevent us from seeing the poverty that specific Asian American groups, such as the Hmong, Cambodians, and Thais, are more likely to experience (Takei and Sakamoto 2011)?

Prejudices and stereotypes are beliefs that often provide foundations for action in the form of discrimination—that is, the differential allocation of goods, resources, and services, and the limitation of access to full participation in society, based on an individual's membership in a particular social category (Adams et al. 1997). Prejudices and stereotypes exist in the realm of beliefs, and when these beliefs guide the ways in which we treat each other, they produce discrimination. Anyone can be the victim of prejudice, stereotyping, or discrimination, including White people, and for a wide variety of reasons, such as clothing, appearance, accent, and membership in clubs or gangs. Put simply, discrimination is prejudice plus power.

Prejudice, stereotypes, and discrimination are probably what first come to mind when we think about racism. But the study of racism goes far beyond these. Like sexism, racism is a system of oppression. Oppression is more than simply individual beliefs and actions—it involves the systematic devaluing, undermining, marginalizing, and disadvantaging of certain social identity groups in contrast to a privileged norm (Ferber and Samuels 2010). Oppression is based on membership in socially constructed identity categories; it is *not* based on individual characteristics.

One sociologist describes racial oppression as a birdcage: an interlocking network of institutional barriers that prevents escape (Frye 2007). Alternatively, others point out the systemic nature of racial oppression. This view posits that core racist realities, values, and ideologies are manifested in all of the major institutions within society (Feagin 2001, 6). Throughout this text we will demonstrate how race exists both historically and contextually as an ongoing form of inequality that pervades every major social institution, including education, employment, government, health care, family, criminal justice, sports, and leisure. Thinking about oppression as a birdcage helps us to understand how it limits people's lives. For example, the gendered wage gap is just one wire in the birdcage that constrains women. If it were the only wire, women could fly around it and escape. However, women face inequality in the home (in domestic labor, child care, elder care, and more), in education, in health care, in the workplace, in the criminal justice system, and more. They are trapped by an entire system of wires that form a cage.

Racism

Racism is a system of oppression by which those groups with relatively more social power subordinate members of targeted racial groups who have relatively little social power. This subordination is supported by individual actions, cultural values, and norms embedded in stock stories, as well as in the institutional structures and practices of society (National Education Association 2015). It is inscribed in codes of conduct, legal sanctions, and organizational rules and practices. Specifically, racism is the subordination of people of color by those who consider themselves White; by implication, the practice of racism defines Whites as superior and all non-Whites as inferior.

The Sociology of Racism

Racism is systemic. It is not about isolated individual actions; individual actions take place within a broader, systemic, cross-institutional context. People of color may themselves harbor prejudices and discriminate on the basis of race; however, without the larger social and historical context of systemic, systematic differences in power, these individual actions do not constitute racism. While this may seem counterintuitive, keep in mind that we are looking at racism from a sociological perspective, focusing on the importance of social context, research, and group experience, rather than on individual behavior. Individual experiences of race and racism will vary. We find it less important to focus on "racists" than on the social matrix of racism in which we live. Additionally, while White people do not experience racism, they may face oppression based on sexual orientation, class, or other social identities.

Who Practices Racism?

Racism in the United States is directed primarily against Blacks, Asian Americans, Latino/as, and Native Americans. Some argue that Muslims may also be considered targets of racism, as they are becoming a racialized group. Racism is the basis of conflict and violence in societies throughout the world, and the forms it takes are varied. Racism is practiced by Whites against Blacks, Coloreds, and Indians in South Africa; by Islamic Arabs against Black Christians in the Sudan; by East Indians against Blacks in Guyana; by those of Spanish descent against those of African and Indian descent in Brazil and Paraguay; by White "Aryans" against Jews and the Romani (Gypsies) in Germany; by the Japanese against the Eta, or Burakumin, in Japan; and by Whites against Africans, Sikhs, Muslims, and Hindus in Great Britain. Racism can take many forms, and it changes over time.

Types of Racism

Formal or overt racism occurs when discriminatory practices and behaviors are sanctioned by official rules, codes, or laws of an organization, institution, or society. Many of the most obvious forms of racism are no longer legally or openly accepted in U.S. society. Such racist practices as slavery, Jim Crow laws, the Black codes, the Indian Removal Act, the internment of Japanese residents during World War II, and the Chinese Exclusion Act are now condemned (but also too conveniently forgotten). Debate is ongoing regarding whether or not other practices—such as immigration policy, the display of the Confederate flag, and the use of American Indian sports mascots—are racist in intent or impact.

Informal or covert racism is subtle in its application, and often ignored or misdiagnosed. It acts informally in that it is assumed to be part of the natural, legitimate, and normal workings of society and its institutions. Thus, when we discuss student learning outcomes we may talk about poor motivation, inadequate schools, or broken homes. We ignore that these characteristics are also typically associated with poor Black and Latino/a neighborhoods (Coates 2011). Microaggressions are subtle insults (verbal, nonverbal, and/or visual) directed toward individuals

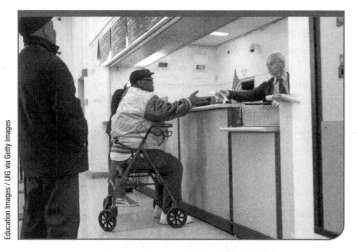

Education Images / UIG via Getty Images

The subtle insults known as microaggressions are common in everyday interactions, like at the post office, even when things seem fine on the surface.

of oppressed social groups, sometimes made unconsciously. Research on college campuses finds that even when things look fine on the surface, inequality and discrimination still manifest themselves in "subtle and hidden forms" that shape interactions and experiences in dorms, class-rooms, dining halls, and student health centers. Over time, these can affect students' performance, and even their mental and physi-cal health (we discuss micro-aggressions in more depth in Chapter 5).

Understanding Privilege

When we study racism, we most often study the experiences of marginalized and oppressed groups. However, everyone's life is shaped by race. Privilege is the flip side of oppression—it involves the systemic favoring, valuing, validating, and including of certain social identities over others. Whiteness is a privileged status.

The Privilege of Whiteness

To be White is to have greater access to rewards and valued resources simply because of group membership. Because they exist in relationship to each other, oppression and privilege operate hand in hand; one cannot exist without the other. Just like oppression, privilege is based on group memberships, not individual factors. We do not choose to be the recipients of oppression or privilege, and we cannot opt out of either one. A White person driving down the street cannot ask the police to pull her over because of her race. Experiences of racism can affect some people and not oth-ers independent of their desires and behaviors.

Making Whiteness visible by acknowledging privilege allows us to examine the ways in which all White people, not just those we identify as "racist," benefit from their racial categorization. Accepting the fact that we live in a society that is immersed in systems of oppression can be difficult, because it means that despite our best intentions, we all participate in perpetuating inequality. In fact, privilege is usually invisible to the people who experience it until it is pointed out. The reality is that White people do not need to think about race very often. Their social location becomes both invisible and the assumed norm.

Research on White privilege has grown over the past three decades, along with the interdisciplinary subfield of Whiteness studies. Works by literary theorists, legal scholars, anthropologists, historians, psychologists, and sociologists alike have contributed to this burgeoning field (Brodkin 1998; Case 2013; Jacobson 1998; Haney López 2006; Moore, Penick-Parks, and Michael 2015; Morrison 1992). However, people of color have been writing about White privilege for a long time. Discussions of White privilege are found in the works of writers such as W. E. B. Du Bois, Anna Julia Cooper, and Ida B. Wells.

Whites are seen as the average, normal, universal human: the "mythical norm" (Lorde [1984] 2007). Descriptions in newspapers and books assume that subjects are White unless other racial identities are made clear. Some were outraged when Noma Dumezweni was cast as Hermione Granger in *Harry Potter and the Cursed Child*, despite the character's race being neither relevant nor specified in the Harry Potter series.

Peggy McIntosh's (1988) classic article "White Privilege and Male Privilege" was one of the first attempts by a White person to document the unearned advantages that Whites experience on a daily basis. For example, White privilege means being able to assume that most of the people you or your children study with in school will be of the same race; being able to go shopping without being followed around in the store; never being called a credit to your race; and being able to find "flesh-colored" bandages to match your skin color. McIntosh also identifies a second type of privilege that gives one group power over another. This conferred dominance legitimates privileges that no one should have in a society that values social justice and equity, such as the right to "own" another human being.

Most of us are the beneficiaries of at least one form of privilege, and often many more. Recognizing this often leads people to feel guilt and shame. However, privilege is derived from group membership; it is not the result of anything we have done as individuals. We are born into these systems of privilege and oppression; we did not create them. Once we become aware of them, though, we must be accountable and work to create change. We can choose whether to acknowledge privilege as it operates in our lives, and whether to use it as a means of creating social change. As Shelly Tochluk (2008, 249–50) notes, this requires that we "begin with personal investigation. . . . If we are going to take a stand, we need to feel prepared to deal with our own sense of discomfort and potential resistance or rejection from others."

The Impact of Stock Stories

The enduring stock story of the United States as a meritocracy makes it very difficult for us to see inequality as institutionalized (McNamee and Miller 2014). An "oppression-blind" belief system ignores the reality of inequality based on social group memberships and sees the United States as the land of equal opportunity, where anyone who works hard can succeed (Ferber 2012).

It is no wonder that individuals, especially those who are most privileged, often resist acknowledging the reality of ongoing inequality. We are immersed in a culture where the ideology of oppression blindness is pervasive. The news and entertainment media bombard us with color-blind "depictions of race relations that suggest that discriminatory racial barriers have been dismantled" (Gallagher 2009, 548). However, these institutionalized barriers still exist. Individuals often experience some cognitive dissonance when confronted with the concept of privilege. We often turn to our familiar stock stories to explain how we feel, countering with responses like "The United States is a meritocracy!" or "Racism is a thing of the past!" Table 1.2 lists some common responses, informed by our stock stories, to learning about privilege (Ferber and Samuels 2010). Do you share any of these feelings?

While our stock stories serve the interests of the dominant group, they are a part of our socialization and social fabric and become perceived as natural, normal, and the way of the world. It is easy to forget that these stories were created at specific moments to justify specific sets of interactions. Race, as part of our structured social system, has become realized as residential segregation, differential educational outcomes, income gaps, racially stratified training and occupational outcomes, social stigmas, and restrictions on social relationships (Smedley 2007, 21–22).

It is only through a deliberate process of critical inquiry that we can deconstruct these seemingly normal relationships to reveal the intentional and unintentional processes of construction and their underlying context. Critical sociological inquiry into the creation and maintenance of difference helps make the familiar strange, the natural unnatural, and the obvious not so obvious, and, in a world where things are often not what they seem, it allows us to see more clearly and deeply.

■ OUR STORIES

As we learn to understand ourselves and others, we can break down the divisions between us and build a foundation for transformative stories and new relationships. That is our goal for you, and we have designed this textbook to guide you through that

Table 1.2 ■ Feeling Race: Understanding Privilege

"I don't feel privileged, my life is hard too!"	This is an example of minimizing or denying privilege (Johnson 2006). We often focus on our oppressed identities as a means of ignoring our privilege.
"My family didn't own slaves!"	As historians have documented, "Into the mid-nineteenth century, the majority of whites—in the elites and among ordinary folk—either participated directly in slavery or in the trade around slavery, or did not object to those who did so" (Feagin 2000, 15). The economies of many northern cities were based almost entirely on the slave trade, and generations of Whites have reaped "undeserved enrichment" from the forced labor of slaves, the cheap labor of other minority group members, and the land and resources taken, often violently, from Native Americans and Mexicans. These practices contribute directly to today's tremendous racial wealth gap.
"I treat everyone the same!"	This type of response shifts the focus to prejudiced and bigoted individuals and allows us to ignore systemic oppression and privilege, and our own role in their reproduction.
"Anyone could succeed if they would just try harder!"	This adherence to the myth of meritocracy attributes the failures of an individual solely to that individual without taking into account systemic inequalities that create an unfair system. It is a form of blaming the victim (Johnson 2006).
"We need to move on! If we would just stop talking about it, it wouldn't be such a big problem!"	Systemic inequalities exist, and ignoring them will not make them go away. As Justice Harry Blackmun stated in his opinion in the U.S. Supreme Court case of *University of California v. Bakke* (1978) some 40 years ago, "In order to get beyond racism, we must first take account of race. There is no other way" (para. 14).
"Stop being so sensitive! I didn't mean it."	Speaking in a derogatory manner about a person or group of people based on social group memberships can have a devastating impact (Sue 2010). Disconnecting our own language or actions is another form of resistance because it minimizes the indiscretion and sends the message that anyone who challenges the language or behavior is simply being overly sensitive.
"I am just one person, I can't change anything!"	Seeing ourselves as incapable of creating change is a means of excusing ourselves from accepting any responsibility and denies agency.

CRITICAL THINKING

1. Racism is dynamic across geographic and social places and across historical periods. Consider some recent events either in the news or at your university: How do they reflect these dynamic processes? (*Hint:* Do you believe that the same types of events would have taken place, say, 50 years ago?)

2. Consider some common stereotypes about athletes, academics, or other professionals. Can you identify any racial stereotypes about which groups might be better at certain sports, disciplines, or professions? What might account for the prevalence of these stereotypes? Do you believe that they have changed over time, or that they would be similar to those in, say, England or Nigeria? What may account for either the similarities or the differences you observe?

3. At your institution are there any student groups that appear to have greater access to rewards and resources than other groups do? If so, what might account for their privilege?

4. Are there any common features (racial or gender or class) among the privileged student groups that you can identify? If so, what does this suggest about privilege?

process. We will journey together to see ourselves, each other, and our society at a deeper level. Our goal is not only to share information and knowledge about the dynamics of race and racism but also to connect this knowledge with our individual lives.

Now, we want to share some of our own stories. Race is deeply personal for each one of us, yet, as sociologists, we have learned much more about ourselves by situating our own lives within a broader context. We hope to help you do the same. We are all situated somewhere in the matrix, so this text is about each of us. We are all in this together.

Rodney

My grandfather was a sharecropper from Yazoo, Mississippi. In 1917, he arrived in East St. Louis, Illinois, a city with a robust industrial base that benefited significantly from World War I, and where much of the mostly White labor force was either in the military or on strike. Many Black men were migrating to East St. Louis at the time, looking for work.

White organized labor, fearful of losing job security, became hostile and targeted the new arrivals. On May 28, at a White union meeting, rumors began circulating that Black men were forcibly seducing and raping White women. A mob of more than 3,000 White men left this meeting and began beating random Black men on the street. The violence claimed the life of a 14-year-old boy, his mother was scalped, and 244 buildings were destroyed—all before the governor called in the National Guard. Rumors continued to circulate, and Blacks were selectively attacked by roving groups of White vigilantes.

But it wasn't over. On July 1, 1917, a Black man attacked a White man. The retaliatory response by Whites was massive, and an entire section of the Black community was destroyed while the police and fire departments refused to respond. My grandfather said that "blood ran like water through the streets." Many residents were lynched, and the entire Black section of the city was burned. No Whites have ever been charged with or convicted of any of these crimes. For the next 50 years, segregation maintained an uneasy peace in this troubled city.

Rodney Coates

Racial segregation, not only in housing but also in hospitals, dictated that I could not be born in the city where my parents resided (East St. Louis, Illinois), because the only hospital that would allow Negro women access was in St. Louis, Missouri. I grew up in a segregated city and went to all-Black elementary, middle, and high schools. Since mainstream educational institutions tended not to hire Black professionals, many of my English, math, and science teachers had advanced degrees, so I received the equivalent of a private education. Given my Blackness and the presumption that I would be a laborer and not a scholar, I also was equally trained in carpentry and sheet metal work. A system designed to keep the races separate provided an outstanding education—one that I was more than ready to take advantage of during the height of the civil rights movement.

After the first wave of racial violence in East St. Louis in 1917, in which hundreds of buildings were burned and a boy was killed, the governor called in the National Guard, seen here escorting a Black citizen through the rubble.

Bettmann / Bettmann / Getty Images

The landmark U.S. Supreme Court decision in *Brown v. Board of Education* (1954) had desegregated the schools, and suddenly places like Southern Illinois University, the University of Illinois, and the University of Chicago were open to someone like me, a kid from a city that would soon become defined as a ghetto. As Blacks asserted their rights and the courts supported them, more doors opened to Blacks, and many Whites began to flee to the suburbs. This White flight, and the loss of business and industries, served to create ghettos where just a few short years before there had been thriving urban centers. I eventually obtained a bachelor's degree, two master's degrees, and a PhD from some of the best educational institutions in this country. My story has sensitized me to the ways in which race, class, and gender are intertwined in the great American narrative. I specialize in critical pedagogy, critical race theory, race and ethnic relations, stratification, human rights and social justice, educational sociology, political processes, urban sociology, political sociology, and public sociology.

Abby

I never had reason to think about race, or my own racial identity as White, until I became a graduate student. Instead, throughout my childhood, my Jewish identity was much more salient. My family was not very religious, but we were "cultural Jews." Growing up in a White, Jewish, upper-middle-class suburb of Cleveland, Ohio (one of the most segregated U.S. cities), I attended religious school on Sunday mornings and services at the synagogue on the High Holy Days. I learned about the Holocaust, the Inquisition, and the long history of pogroms. When I was in elementary school, the school building was bombed one night, and anti-Semitic epithets were scrawled on the walls. The message I internalized was that Jews were the universal scapegoat, and even when they were fully assimilated and successful, their safety was never secure. So even though I have never considered myself religious, I learned that what often matters more is whether other people see me as Jewish.

Abby Ferber

My great-grandmother fled her small Russian village when she was 16 years old to avoid an arranged marriage. Her parents disowned her, and she never spoke to them again. After she immigrated to the United States, she learned that her entire family had perished in concentration camps. My grandmother grew up in a Catholic community where her Jewish family was ostracized. At Ohio State University in the 1960s, my mother's roommate asked to see her horns. Last year, on a family vacation with my adolescent daughter, another member of our tour group took the guide's microphone and entertained the group with anti-Semitic jokes.

Yet I am also the beneficiary of White privilege, and this has had a greater impact on my life. I have never had to worry about being pulled over by police, not getting a job, or not being able to rent or purchase a home because of my race. I did not have to teach my daughter how to behave around the police for her own security. As Jews became defined as White, my grandparents were able to take out loans and start a small business. My parents were both able to attend college. Today, Jews are accepted as White in the United States.

In the years before and after World War II, many Jews fled their homes in Russia and Europe. These Jewish immigrants from Eastern Europe sought visas at the U.S. embassy in Paris, hoping to reach the United States.

My dissertation research examined the construction of race and gender in the context of the organized White supremacist movement. My research made my White privilege much more visible and real to me, ironically, because for White supremacists I am *not* White. Their ideology lumps Jews into the broad category of non-Whites, along with African Americans, Latinos, and Asian Americans. Studying this movement was the first time I really became aware of my White privilege, as I finally understood that it could be taken away. Privilege and oppression are not the result of anything a person has done as an individual. For instance, I have no control over who recognizes me as White or non-White, or when.

I also grew up acutely aware of gender oppression, even if I did not have the language to name it. I experienced sexual harassment at every job I held between middle school and graduate school, experienced numerous attempted rapes, and have received unequal pay compared to men doing the same job as me.

As a graduate student, I first learned about privilege and intersectionality, and this provided a framework that allowed me to better understand the complexity of who I am, not only a Jewish female, but a White, heterosexual, middle-class, temporarily able-bodied and -minded, Jewish woman. I now have a greater understanding of

Goshen College is a Mennonite institution that focuses on outreach, study abroad, and missionary and/or "development" work.

David Brunsma

how all of those identities intersect in shaping my life experience. And I now realize, as a person who benefits from White privilege, that it is my responsibility to work to reduce racial inequality. I never experienced guilt or shame when I learned of my privilege, but instead started asking how I could be a part of the solution.

Dave

I was born in Des Moines, Iowa, to a Puerto Rican mother and a largely unknown White father. My mother and her brothers and sisters had been adopted and raised by my solidly White, privileged, Christian grandparents in mostly White neighborhoods. While there were some variations in the degree of Puerto Rican identity felt among my family members, by and large they were White. I too was raised White. I have come to embrace my Puerto Rican identity, but I did not really know about it until the stories and structures of my life were already quite fully built along White lines.

As I grew up, although I delved into critical literatures, music, and film outside the scope of public school and family, it was expected that I would be White—talk White, dress White, and, ultimately, think and live White. I was also destined to reproduce the structures of White privilege and racism, despite the fact that I could see them then, and can see them even more clearly now. My life as a White American preordained my complacency and tacit agreement with the exploitative racial contract in White America, even while I fully disagree with it.

I went to a Mennonite college that preaches a kind of liberation theology, from which many go on to serve in missionary or "development" capacities all around the world—with good intentions but often ending up as color-blind extensions of American (or Jesus) imperialism. There were few people of color there, or in graduate school. Meanwhile, my critical, social justice lenses were becoming more sharply focused. I am still learning to "see" myself, my story, my place in the matrix; this is an important step in seeing others deeply as well. My research is focused on (multi)racial identity, race and ethnicity, human rights, sociology of education, and the sociology of culture.

CRITICAL THINKING

1. Each of us has a story. In what ways does your story reflect a particular narrative? How might your story be different from the stories of your parents or grandparents, or from those of your peers?

2. Are you a first-generation college student or did your parents also attend college? How are your college experiences different from their experiences (either as students or not)?

3. In what ways might your race, class, and gender affect your experiences? What does this suggest about how time and space interact with identity?

4. What changes do you envision for your children or the next generation? What stories do you think they will tell? And how might they interpret your story?

KEY TERMS

CHAPTER SUMMARY

LO 1.1 Explain how race and ethnicity are socially constructed.

Race changes over time and across geographical spaces. It is an unstable and shifting concept. The U.S. Census Bureau attempts to identify the major racial groups in the United States, but it changes its definitions often. Defining a race is an example of the process of "Othering." Ethnicity and panethnicity are much more nuanced and layered concepts than those reflected in typical race categories. Within the United States, White ethnics have consistently been dominant, in terms of power as well as in numbers. This dominance owes its origins to practices, ideologies, and institutions that derive from our colonial past. And these practices, ideologies, and institutions have served to reinforce racial categorizations while obscuring the fluidity of race and ethnicity. Race definitions, structures, and practices are not applied consistently across the globe.

LO 1.2 Evaluate the relationship between social contexts and race.

The social context of race illustrates the reality of race in our society. Our focus on race helps us to understand how it shapes our identities, institutions, societies, and prospects for change. We use the concept of the matrix of race to help us see how the social construction of race is realized within our society. Our identities intersect along race, gender, and other axes, and these intersectional identities operate across various institutional and geographical spaces and historical periods. Looking at race in the social matrix highlights it as a social construct, as narrative, as relational and intersectional, and as institutional and structural, and it also emphasizes the role of humans as active agents in the process of racialization.

LO 1.3 Identify the concepts and operation of racism.

We use a variety of narrative types to highlight the operation and potential for transformation of race and racial structures. Our stock stories narrate how reality works. These stories often obscure or legitimate various types of oppression. Concealed stories are uncovered as we attempt to understand the actual ways in which race operates. By uncovering these narratives we often become aware of stories of resistance (where individuals or groups have attempted to circumvent or overcome racial structures) and/or stories of transformation (where individuals or groups have actually facilitated changes to race and racial structures). Prejudice, stereotyping, and discrimination, which anyone may encounter, are part of racism, but racism reaches beyond those practices and is systematic and institutional. Racism is a system of oppression.

LO 1.4 Examine the link between our personal narratives and the broader "story" of race.

We all have stories. Understanding our own narratives helps us examine how race, the matrix, and intersectionality operate within our lives.

THE SHAPING OF A NATION

The Social Construction of Race in America

John Moore / Getty Images News / Getty Images

Hundreds of Sudanese refugees have fled civil war and settled in the U.S., where they have a great deal to learn. Many cities have nonprofit organizations dedicated to helping these refugees acclimate to their new home towns.

CHAPTER OUTLINE

LEARNING OBJECTIVES

LO 2.1   Explore how recent events have affected how we experience race.

LO 2.2   Describe the Americas before Columbus.

LO 2.3   Examine the patterns of Spanish, French, and British colonialism in the Americas.

LO 2.4   Evaluate the intersections of race, identities, institutions, and resistance.

Thon Marial Maker was born in the midst of the Sudanese civil war in 1997. He fled the turmoil, along with some family members, and escaped into Uganda. From there he immigrated as a refugee into Australia. At the age of 14, Maker was discovered by Edward Smith, an Australian basketball coach who works with children from immigrant backgrounds to help them excel in the sport. Smith had previously worked with Ater Majok and Mathiang Muo, who went on to become professional basketball players, Majok for the Los Angeles Lakers and Muo for the Perth Wildcats in Western Australia. Smith offered Maker and his family the same opportunities, providing food, clothing, and education. In 2011, Maker and

Smith traveled to Texas to attend a basketball talent camp, where he was recruited to play. Maker played high school basketball first in Louisiana, then at Carlisle High School in Martinsville, Virginia. He was named the Gatorade Virginia Boys Basketball Player of the Year in 2014. The following year, cable sports channel ESPN ranked him as the top high school basketball player in the United States (Biancardi 2015). He was drafted by the Milwaukee Bucks in 2016. As a pro, Maker has averaged 9.6 rebounds and 14.2 points per game (Gardner 2017).

Maker was one of the almost 20,000 Sudanese boys uprooted because of civil war over the past three decades. Of this group, who have come to be known as the Lost Boys of Sudan, some 4,000 came to the United States. Hundreds would eventually settle in areas such as Atlanta, Boston, Dallas, Phoenix, Salt Lake City, San Diego, Seattle, and Tucson. Maker and the Lost Boys joined millions of immigrants who have come to the United States seeking peace, justice, freedom, and the American Dream. Their story is at the heart of our story and the shaping of a nation. As we will see, it is a story that has defined the racial matrix, created intersectionality, and set us on the path that we continue to walk to this day.

■ RACE TODAY: ADAPTING AND EVOLVING

Turn on a television, scroll your social media feed, or watch any movie, and you will discover that it is almost impossible to avoid the conclusion that race is intricately involved in most current events and issues. In fact, it often seems that our nation is consumed with race. How did we get here, and what does this obsession suggest about who we are as a people? In this chapter we will discuss the unique set of circumstances that started us down this path. But first, let's take a look at the current realities of race. While race seems both elusive and static, it is continually adapting and evolving.

Changing Demographics

The United States, as a nation of immigrants, has historically been defined by racial and ethnic diversity. Close to 60 million immigrants have arrived in the United States over the past 50 years. In 2016, nearly 14% of U.S. residents were foreign-born, most hailing from Latin America and Asia (Cohn and Caumont 2016).

The U.S. population is projected to grow from 422 million to 458 million in the next 40 years. During this period, as the baby boomers—that is, those who are part of the demographic group born right after World War II—age, our nation will also become slightly older. The proportion of the population made up of people age 65 and older will increase from 13% to about 20%. During this same period, total births will reach their highest level, with an estimated 4.3 million births. Much of this increase will be due to recent immigrants, who average higher fertility rates than the general population. The proportion of the population ages 15 to 64 is also expected to increase by 42% (Kotkin 2010).

Figure 2.1 ■ The Face of America is Changing

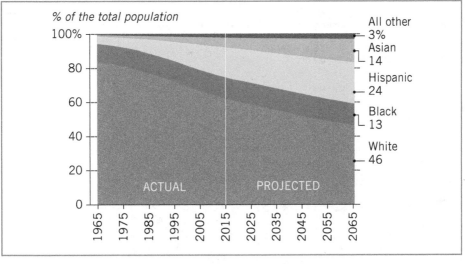

% of the total population

All other — 3%
Asian — 14
Hispanic — 24
Black — 13
White — 46

ACTUAL   PROJECTED

1965 1975 1985 1995 2005 2015 2025 2035 2045 2055 2065

more diverse

Source: D'Vera Cohn and Andrea Caumont, "10 Demographic Trends That Are Shaping the U.S. and the World," Fact Tank, Pew Research Center, March 31, 2016, http://www.pewresearch.org/fact-tank/2016/03/31/10-demographic-trends-that-are-shaping-the-u-s-and-the-world.

These demographic changes will have significant impacts on most of our institutions. As we will see in Chapter 10, the 2016 electorate was the most diverse in U.S. history, and it was the increasing growth in the numbers of racial minority voters that gave Barack Obama victories in both 2008 and 2012. But while younger voters are becoming increasingly diverse, one of the fastest-growing voting groups consists of the older Americans of the baby boomer generation. Donald Trump's 2016 election victory was a result of these older voters supporting him with 53% of their votes (Tyson and Maniam 2016).

These demographic changes will also have an immediate impact on colleges and universities across the nation. We can forecast these trends by examining the current racial makeup of grade school classrooms. In 2014, for the first time, the number of Latinos, African Americans, Asian Americans, Pacific Islanders, and Native Americans combined exceeded the number of Whites in public grade school classrooms (Williams 2014). Non-Hispanic Whites are currently in the minority in the populations of four states: California (which has a 61% minority population), Hawaii (77% minority), New Mexico (61% minority), and Texas (56% minority). And Nevada (48.5% minority), Maryland (47.4% minority), and Georgia (45% minority) are not that far behind (Maciag 2015).

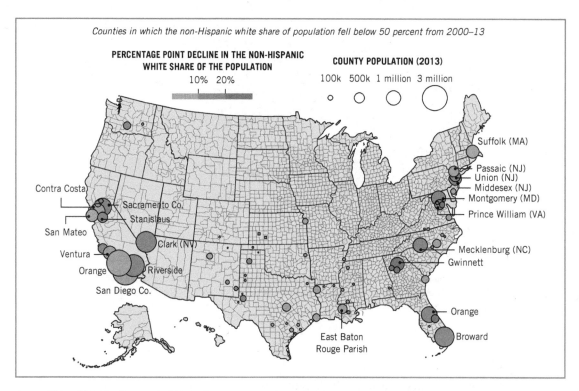

Counties in which the non-Hispanic white share of population fell below 50 percent from 2000–13

PERCENTAGE POINT DECLINE IN THE NON-HISPANIC WHITE SHARE OF THE POPULATION
10% 20%

COUNTY POPULATION (2013)
100k 500k 1 million 3 million

Suffolk (MA)
Passaic (NJ)
Union (NJ)
Middesex (NJ)
Montgomery (MD)
Prince William (VA)
Mecklenburg (NC)
Gwinnett
Orange
Broward
East Baton Rouge Parish
Contra Costa
Sacramento Co.
Stanislaus
San Mateo
Ventura
Orange
Riverside
San Diego Co.
Clark (NV)

Source: "Where Minorities Became the Majority Between 2000 and 2013." In "Reflecting a Racial Shift, 78 Counties Turned Majority-Minority since 2000," by Jens Manuel Krogstad, Pew Research Center Fact Tank, April 8, 2015. http://www.pewresearch.org/fact-tank/2015/04/08/reflecting-a-racial-shift-78-counties-turned-majority-minority-since-2000.

Figure 2.2 shows that since 2000, 78 counties in 19 U.S. states became majority-minority. Of these, 14 had been at least 60% White (Krogstad 2015).

The most diverse counties are concentrated in California, in the South, and on the East Coast. And in 19 of the 25 largest U.S. counties (measured by population), Whites made up less than half of the population. Six of these that were majority White in 2000 are no longer so. These are San Diego, Orange, Riverside, and Sacramento Counties in California; Clark County, Nevada; Broward County, Florida (Krogstad 2015). As such changes take place, they will have impacts on everything from work and the economy to family structures to who serves in the military. Our media and other forms of entertainment, including sports, will also be affected. Some impacts are even now becoming apparent.

The Influence of a Changing World

The United States has been experiencing a particularly turbulent period since the September 11, 2001, terrorist attacks that resulted in the deaths of more than 3,000 people. This single event has fundamentally altered the experiences of everyone in this country and in the world. During this period we have also witnessed four separate wars, as well as countless other military operations from Haiti to Libya, Afghanistan to Iraq—many of them rooted in notions of "the Other" and difference.

During the past few decades, ethnic violence has erupted into genocide—the large-scale, systematic destruction of a people or nation—among the Tutsis and Hutus in Rwanda and among the Serbs, Croats, and Muslims in Bosnia. Racial violence, violence that pits one racial group against another, has occurred around the world, including in places like Australia, India, Belgium, France, and the United Kingdom. Closer to home, riots and civil unrest stemming from issues of race have disrupted a number of U.S. cities, including Cincinnati, Ohio (2001); Benton Harbor, Michigan (2003); Oakland, California (2009); Hempstead, New York (2010); Ferguson, Missouri (2014–15); and Baltimore, Maryland (2015). And we have witnessed the public reactions to violence between police forces and people of color, reactions that reveal our anxieties and frustrations about race.

After Freddie Gray, a 25-year-old Black Baltimorean, died from injuries he sustained while in police custody in 2015, the city erupted in protests.

Not all of the change has been violent. We have also witnessed several firsts for women and persons of color. Many of you may have experienced the euphoria of the 2003 launch of the space shuttle *Columbia,* carrying possibly the most diverse flight crew ever seen, and also experienced the tragedy of that crew's loss as the shuttle disintegrated during reentry. We celebrated the fall of the Berlin Wall in 1989, and the election of the first Black president of the United States in 2008. In 2005, the deadly force of Hurricane Katrina revealed the ugly underbelly of race, class, and gender as thousands of New Orleans residents were displaced—the largest internal displacement in American history (Kromm and Sturgis 2008). America has discovered new phrases such as "racial profiling," "subprime loans," and "dining while Black"—all of which demonstrate our continued obsession and problems associated with difference and solidify the idea that each of us experiences the world from our own position within the matrix (Goyette and Scheller 2016). Compared to Americans living in previous periods, we are generally more fashion conscious, upbeat, diverse, liberal, confident, self-expressive, and open to change (Taylor and Keeter 2010). As we learned earlier, Latinos are quickly emerging as a population that is significantly altering what it means to be American, and college enrollment among Hispanics is now the largest and fastest growing of all student groups (Fry 2011).

Revising the Experience of Work, Gender, and Race

Women currently make up only about 4% of CEOs in Fortune 500 firms, and Asians, Hispanics, and Blacks account for slightly more than 1% (Zarya 2016). Alongside some gains, women of all social groups have on average lost ground over the past few years due to the triple glass ceiling, or three-pronged workplace discrimination based on race, gender, and class (Gutiérrez, Meléndez, and Noyola 2007). This and other disparities have been aggravated by the financial recession that began in 2008.

Wage disparities affect all women, but Hispanic, African American, American Indian, Native Hawaiian, and other native women are the lowest paid. For the women in these groups, however, the gender gap—the difference between their wages and those of men in the same groups—is not as great as the gap for White non-Hispanic women, who experience the largest gender gap.

Closer examination reveals that among all groups, Hispanic women, followed by African American women, have the largest earning gap when compared to White men (54% and 63%, respectively). These gaps increase with age: Median earnings of women ages 16–19 are 89% of the earnings of their male counterparts, compared to 74% for those 65 and older. Finally, while education does improve the earnings of women of all races and ethnicities, racial and gendered differences remain. Among educated women, Asian Americans lead all other women in median annual earnings regardless of education.

Sources of Change and Diversity

Although Americans as a nation are more diverse than ever before, many of us find our realities still structured by race. For instance, White students are only slightly less likely than students of previous generations to attend nearly all-White primary and secondary schools, while minority students, including Latino and Black students, are actually more likely to attend nearly all-minority schools (Childress 2014). In fact, some researchers have documented that American primary and secondary schools are even more segregated by race and class today than they were in the late 1950s after the landmark Supreme Court desegregation case *Brown v. Board of*

Education of Topeka, Kansas (Orfield 2009). This apparent contradiction is a by-product of the civil rights movement, which led more affluent families of color to move from the cities to the suburbs, while urban schools became increasingly less diverse. As middle-class women and women of color have, on average, reversed the achievement gap for college completion and graduate school admissions, among lower-class women and men of color these gaps have become even more entrenched. As a result of these shifts, young Latinos for the first time now outnumber young Blacks on campus, even though Black college enrollment has also grown steadily for decades, and it, too, has surged in recent years (Fry 2011).

The Evolving Narrative of Popular Culture

Two recent popular book series, J. K. Rowling's *Harry Potter* series and Stephenie Meyer's *Twilight* saga, demonstrate how race, class, and gender issues prevail even in fictional universes (Moje, Young, Readence, and Moore 2000; Strommen and Mates 2004). Some of the allure of the *Twilight* series might be that it weaves together concerns about sex, race, and class as the human protagonist violates racial-like norms and falls in love with a vampire. The story suggests that our society can overcome both racism and sexism in this fictionalized world where vampires, werewolves, and humans get along and battle for gender equality (Wilson 2011). Unfortunately, this fictionalized social reality is just that—fictionalized (Bonilla-Silva 2008). Other popular books feature worlds where race, power, oppression, and liberation are clearly etched into the narratives. Take the case of the *Harry Potter* books, which present a strikingly racialized narrative where the world is divided among the "pure-blood" wizarding families; the "half-bloods," or wizards born of nonwizarding families, and the "Muggles," or nonmagical humans.

The Impact of Social *a lot!!!* Media and Technology

About 7 out of 10 Americans now use online social networks (Perrin 2015). You might assume that our online experiences would reflect society's increasingly diverse demographic structure. However, research shows that even online, our experiences are structured by race, class, and gender. Facebook friendships among college students are not only more likely to be among those living in the same dorm

In recent years the international phenomenon of the *Hunger Games* trilogy has brought the topics of the structures of inequality, the excesses of power, and the promises of liberation struggles and uprisings back into the popular discourse.

and studying the same subject but also self-segregated by gender, race, class, and even hometown (Lewis, Gonzalez, and Kaufman 2011). Rather than challenging the racial status quo, the online world has ultimately reproduced it. Perhaps it is not so strange that this is so; human beings have been grappling with issues of difference since the dawn of civilization.

With more than 316 million residents and a history of immigration that goes back more than 500 years, to long before the founding of the nation, the United States is one of the most ethnically and racially diverse countries in the world. We are a nation of immigrants. While English is the dominant language, more than 300 other languages are spoken here (Shin and Kominski 2010). In fact, the United States has no official language. Examining the nation's story helps us understand why.

CRITICAL THINKING QUESTIONS

1. Why do current demographic shifts define us as a nation? How might these changes differ across different geographical areas?

2. How do demographic shifts affect various social institutions?

3. How might future demographic changes affect different areas and institutions? How can social media become an instrument of change?

4. How will the demographic evolution affect you? Are you ready for the changes that are coming?

■ INDIGENOUS PEOPLES: THE AMERICAS BEFORE COLUMBUS

As a nation, we rely on certain stories to bind us together, the most central of which has to do with the founding and discovery of our country—our own "stock story":

In fourteen hundred and ninety-two, Columbus sailed the ocean blue.

According to this story, a brave and daring Christopher Columbus set off from Europe with three ships to find a shorter route to Asia. Columbus, often portrayed as a scientific and astronomical genius, proved not only that the world is round but also that its circumnavigation was feasible.

Figure 2.3 ■ European Colonization Began with Viking Exploration in 986

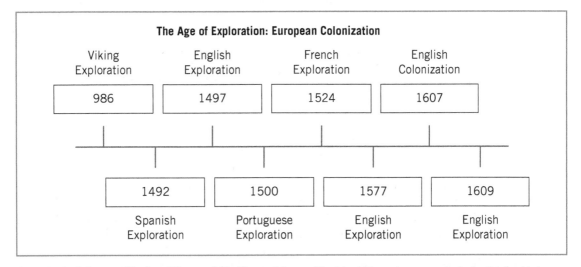

Source: Kimberly Burgess, "The Age of Discovery," http://theageofdiscoverykbsp14.weebly.com/european-colonization-timeline.html.

Recent historical revisions have challenged this story, suggesting that this "discovery" was more like an invasion. Though vastly outnumbered by the natives of the Americas, the Europeans benefited greatly from "guns, germs, and steel"—the superior weaponry and disease-causing microbes they brought from Europe that allowed them to impose their wills on the indigenous Americans (Diamond 1999).

The Earliest Americans

Prior to Columbus, the Americas was inhabited by Native Americans. From the Abenakis of Maine to the Zunis of New Mexico, Native Americans are descendants of an even earlier group of immigrants to the Americas. These Asian immigrants were the first Americans, arriving more than 20,000 years ago. There is a good chance that they came via two different routes:

1. People on foot, traversing the glacial land bridge between Siberia and Alaska, were mostly hunters and gatherers who followed the mastodon and long-horned bison, and might have been responsible for their eventual extinction.

2. Fishers and hunters utilizing boats from the Pacific Islands allowed the currents to guide them to these shores (Arnaiz-Villena et al. 2010).

Many geographical place names help identify the first peoples of the Americas. More than half of U.S. state names are representative of the original inhabitants of those areas. The following are just a few:

- Michigan, from the Allegany language, meaning "big water"

- Minnesota, from the Siouan language, meaning "water that reflects the sky"

- Missouri, from the Siouan language, meaning "water flowing along"

- Ohio, from the Iroquois language, meaning "good river"

Many state names reflect the dominance of particular tribes, such as Massachusetts, Connecticut, Illinois, and Dakota. While Native Americans rarely gave a single name to an entire river or mountain, they typically gave names to specific features, such as the mouth or bend of a particular river. They tended to name each peak or crag rather than the whole mountain. We have many of these names still with us today, such as Potomac (Iroquois, meaning "the place to which tribute is brought") or Allegheny (Iroquois derived from *monongahela*, which means "falling banks").

Native Americans typically gave specific names to each feature of a river or mountain. Many of these names are still in use today.

Many of the early Native American communities were urban, with populations reaching the tens of thousands. Archaeologists and anthropologists have identified several towns, with temples and evidence of a priestly class, along with nobles, merchants, and artisans, demonstrating highly stratified, hierarchical, and technologically sophisticated civilizations.

A Rich History

Hundreds of years before Columbus, North America was home to millions of people and hundreds of population groups, tribes, and linguistic and cultural systems. These people called themselves Iroquois and Mohawk, Miami and Illini, Lakota and Apache, and hundreds of other names. As noted above, many areas in our country retain the names of this rich history. In the Northeast, the Iroquois and the Algonquin, two major language and cultural groups, occupied a region now known as the Northeastern Woodlands. The Algonquin controlled two major areas, one encompassing the Great Lakes and the other near the Atlantic Ocean. Several tribes constituted the Algonquin. The Wampanoag were the first tribe in this region encountered by the Europeans. Both the Illini and the Potawatomi occupied the Illinois region. The League of the Iroquois, formed as early as 1090, comprised five tribes who lived in the areas today known as New York State and the Southeastern Woodlands (which stretched from the Atlantic Ocean to the Mississippi River and from the Gulf of Mexico to the Ohio River). The largest northern groups in the confederation were the Cherokee, the Chickasaw, and the Creek. The southern regions were dominated by the Natchez, Biloxi, and Seminole—known as the Mound Builders (Lord and Burke 1991).

Their histories are reflected in the many names they gave this land—such as the Lakota and Mohawk's Anowarkowa (Turtle Island), the Powhatan's Tsenacommacah (densely inhabited area), and the Shawnee's Kantukee (the great meadow, or the dark and bloody ground). They lived in teepees and huts, cities and villages; they built burial mounds, temples, and multistory buildings. And they routinely and systematically planted and harvested more than 100 kinds of crops (including tomatoes, quinoa, and peaches) using crop-rotation techniques and an understanding of the importance of seasonal flooding for the enrichment of nutrient-poor soil (Mann 2005).

In their farming, these original Americans added charcoal and broken pottery to the tropical red clays—an agricultural method recognized today. Skilled at metallurgy, they examined metals for their malleability and toughness (Mendoza 1997).

The earliest Americans hunted buffalo, boar, turkey, rabbit, and deer. Their diet also included perch, catfish, oysters, and salmon. They mastered carving, weaving, tanning, and pot making. Not only did they develop highly sophisticated artistry in jewelry, weaving, and textiles, but they also created pictorial art on cave walls and rocks. Their works are displayed in some of the finest museums across the world today. These peoples had highly developed written, oral, and symbolic languages; math and calendar systems; religions; political systems; and constitutions. Their civilizations were hundreds of years older than the oldest European nation, richer than we will ever know, and more varied than has ever been captured in the stock stories of "cowboys and Indians."

These Native Americans were neither brutes nor savages, neither pagans nor infidels. They were not prototypical environmentalists or solitary figures in contest with the forces of progress—they were humans, with all of the creative and marvelous social inventions we have come to recognize as human, such as democratic governance and constitutional bodies, federations and confederations, family and community. They had both philosophies and mythologies, prophecies and paradigms, educational systems and beliefs about the cosmos, hopes and dreams. They had wars and civil unrest, and military, political, civil, and religious leaders.

They bartered and traded and had many types of coinage and economies. Ultimately, they lived full, expansive, rich, and complete lives long before Columbus and the Europeans discovered them and entered their matrix to create a new one.

■ DISCOVERY AND ENCOUNTERS: THE SHAPING OF OUR STORIED PAST

European colonization of the Americas actually began in the 10th to 11th centuries, when Viking sailors explored what is currently Canada (Figure 2.3). In their explorations, they settled Greenland, sailed up the Arctic region of North America, and engaged in violent conflict with several indigenous populations. More extensive European colonization began in 1492, when Spanish ships captained by Christopher Columbus inadvertently landed on the northern tip of Cuba. In all instances, colonial adventures were particularly nationalistic, as evidenced by the names of Nueva Española, Nouvelle-France, and New England. Settlement of this so-called New World centered on transplanting, cloning, and grafting European institutions into the Americas. These particularities were aggravated by competition over control of land, ports, raw resources, and native peoples.

Understanding Colonialism

Colonialism is a set of hierarchical relationships in which groups are defined culturally, ethnically, and/or racially, and these relationships serve to guarantee the political, social, and economic interests of the dominant group (Barrera 1976, 3). Under the guise of advancing the "kingdom of God," the Spanish, French, and English pursuit of colonies was more closely aligned with greed and fame.

Religious ideology was used to justify wars of aggression, exploitation, subjugation, extermination, enslavement, and colonization. The structures, ideologies, and actions that form patterns of colonialism shape groups' interrelated experiences in profound ways—the realities behind colonialism are complex, and usually structurally and culturally catastrophic for the colonized. We can view colonialism through three primary lenses:

1. As a structure of domination subjugating one group of people to another across political entities

2. As "internal" or "domestic" colonialism, a similar structure occurring within a given nation-state, typically against socially marked groups

3. As a "colonialism of the mind," wherein the colonized are institutionally, pedagogically, linguistically, and cognitively conquered by the colonizer

The colonies that developed within the Americas are best classified as settler colonies. Settler colonies are distinguished by the colonizing nation's control of political, economic, social, and cultural mechanisms in the colonies, which creates a colonial elite. The European elite who migrated to the settler colonies in the Americas were intent on settlement, creation of a self-sustaining independent political/economic system, and domination of both geography and indigenous populations. Even while settler colonies maintained dependency relationships with their respective European nations, they nevertheless achieved significant autonomy (Stasiulis and Yuval-Davis 1995).

European settlements and population dynamics varied considerably both across different European groups and compared with those established by Native Americans. Pre-Columbian population estimates suggest that Native Americans were generally distributed throughout the Americas, with most occupying the areas that are now Mexico and Central America (47%), followed by South America (35%) and the Caribbean (10%). The remainder were scattered across what would become the United States and Canada. The first groups of colonizers, the Spanish and Portuguese, settled in the most densely populated areas. Later colonizing efforts by both the French and the English created settlements in the less densely populated areas primarily in North America and Canada (Figure 2.4). Such dynamics produced very different sets of opportunities and issues for both the colonizers and the colonized.

Spanish Colonialism (1492)

We must be willing to confront the history of the Americas in terms that are more complex and nuanced than those often provided by simple historical accounts. At no time were the colonies ever fully independent of or politically isolated from what was happening in Europe or among the various Native American nations. In 1492, when Columbus stumbled on a set of islands off the coast of Florida, he named them Hispana, the Latin name for Spain. Despite the fact that this land was home to a significant population, Columbus declared it *terra nullius* (empty land), revealing much about how explorers and, later, colonists saw themselves in relation to others and the world around them.

Constructing a Racial Ideology

The Spanish encountered a significantly different people with specific cultural, political, and gender systems. Native American gender systems varied across tribal groups. Gender relations within the Taino tribes, for example, were both egalitarian and nonexclusive. Women were able to own property and often served as ritual leaders and organized most of the subsistence work (Deagan and Cruxent 2002, 31–32; Deagan 2004).

Figure 2.4 ■ European Colonizers Settled in Distinct Geographic Areas

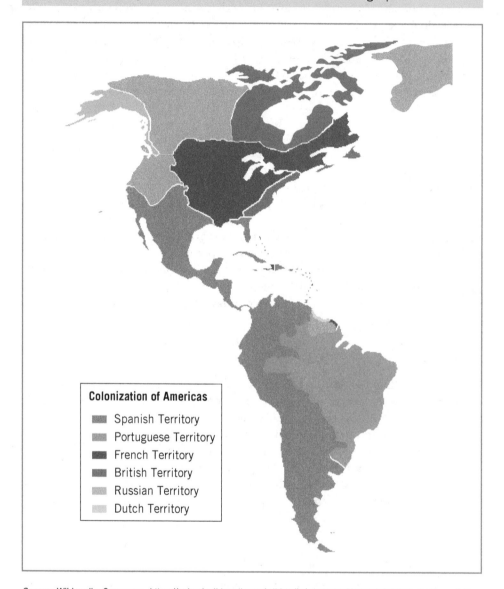

Colonization of Americas

- Spanish Territory
- Portuguese Territory
- French Territory
- British Territory
- Russian Territory
- Dutch Territory

Source: Wikimedia Commons, https://upload.wikimedia.org/wikipedia/commons/thumb/b/b0/Colonization_of_the_Americas_1750.PNG/300px-Colonization_of_the_Americas_1750.PNG.

By 1570, the Spanish colonies were utilizing two racial distinctions:

1. *Spanish-born or –descended:* This group consisted of those born in either Spain or the colonies and included both those of mixed heritage and those considered to be "purebloods."

2. *Native-born or –descended:* This group consisted of all Native Americans, who were considered vassals of the king.

Each of these groups had different rights, obligations, and privileges. Natives, under Spanish laws, were obliged to provide labor for both government and private enterprises deemed vital to colonial interests, and to pay special poll taxes or tributes. While these laws were intended to create two distinct classes, the flexible laws of both marriage and residence allowed many Native Americans to adopt European-style dress and "pass" as purebloods (Jackson 2006, 902).

The Catholic Church, notably through the Spanish Inquisition and the Franciscan order, used purity certifications to impose barriers on some Spaniards who sought to immigrate to the Americas. The church would use these same purity levels to label both Africans and Native Americans as "New Christians" and mark both as "impure" (Martinez 2004, 483). Any offspring of interracial unions involving New Christians would thus be less valued. Put simply, Blacks, Native Americans, and others could be redeemed and baptized, but they still could not mix with "purebloods."

Grounded in vague notions of purity and supposed biological differences, these rules would later become the basis for the racial caste system, a permanent hierarchy based on race, that developed in Spanish America (Martinez 2008). These laws also reveal the centrality of gender relations to the construction of culture and race. In order to distinguish one culture from another and define one as superior, societies must maintain borders. These borders are inscribed onto women's bodies and then policed by regulating sexual relationships. The bodies and wombs of White women were considered sacred—they were the only source of future generations of Whites (Martinez 2008, 483–84). European men, on the other hand, maintained for themselves access to all women's bodies. Ultimately, this racial caste system would be linked to the social and economic hierarchies that exist today in Latin American countries in what scholars refer to as pigmentocracies, as discussed in Chapter 1 (Telles and the Project on Ethnicity and Race in Latin America 2014).

The Slave System

Columbus was the first to employ slavery in the colonies. Two days after he "discovered" America, Columbus wrote in his journal that with 50 men he could order that "the entire population be taken to Castile, or held captive." On his second voyage in December 1494, Columbus captured 1,500 Tainos on the island of Hispaniola and selected 550 of "the best males and females" to be presented to the Spanish queen,

Isabella, and sold in the slave markets of Seville, Spain (Beal 2008, 60). In 1525 a total of 5,271 slaves appeared on the notarial records of Seville; almost 400 were listed as Blacks or mulattoes (Phillips 1985, 161).

The Spanish colonies were considered lenient with regard to racial classification, for multiple reasons:

- The colonial laws accorded protections to Native Americans and to slaves.
- Slaves' rights were protected by both judicial and ecclesiastical authority.
- Spanish slave laws were derived from Roman legal traditions.
- Manumission (the freeing of slaves) did not require prior approval from the crown.
- Slaves could purchase their own freedom.
- Slaves had legal recourse through the Spanish courts, even for grievances against their masters. (Parise 2008, 13–14)

Ultimately, the supply of Native American labor in the Spanish colonies was decimated by continual warfare, disease, and sheer overwork. Under the licensing system established by King Ferdinand in 1513, an estimated 75,000 to 90,000 African slaves were sent to Spanish America by 1600. This figure would more than triple by the end of the 17th century, accounting for approximately 350,000 enslaved Africans (Landers 1997, 85). With these massive increases in the labor force, the Spanish colonies shifted to plantation economies, which also fundamentally altered Spanish slavery. Blacks began to outnumber Whites in Hispaniola and Mexico by an estimated ratio of 10 to 1 by the early to mid-16th century. Many of the medieval slave protections were stripped away, and Spanish officials' worst nightmares were realized as slave insurrections repeatedly threatened one colonial settlement after another.

Black slaves were the major source of labor on sugar plantations in Spanish America, particularly after Native American populations were decimated.

French Colonialism (1534)

New France, the first site colonized by France in North America, was created by the 1534 expedition headed by Jacques Cartier along the Saint Lawrence River in what is now Quebec (Figure 2.5). Cartier's explorations allowed France to claim the land that would later become Canada. The French sought gold along the Saint Lawrence River, but settled for fishing and fur trading instead. And it was here, in 1608, that Quebec was established as the first French colony (Greer 1997, 6).

The French attempted to colonize a large chunk of the Americas with an extremely small and mostly male colonial force. The fact that the Frenchmen were outnumbered and unable to establish cultural dominance and stable communities helps explain their eventual failure.

Among financiers and merchants, the French colonial expansion into the Americas was conceived of as a business venture, and profits were often seen as more important than colonial development. Officially, the primary goal of these ventures was the Christianization of the natives, but it was not until after the first successful

---

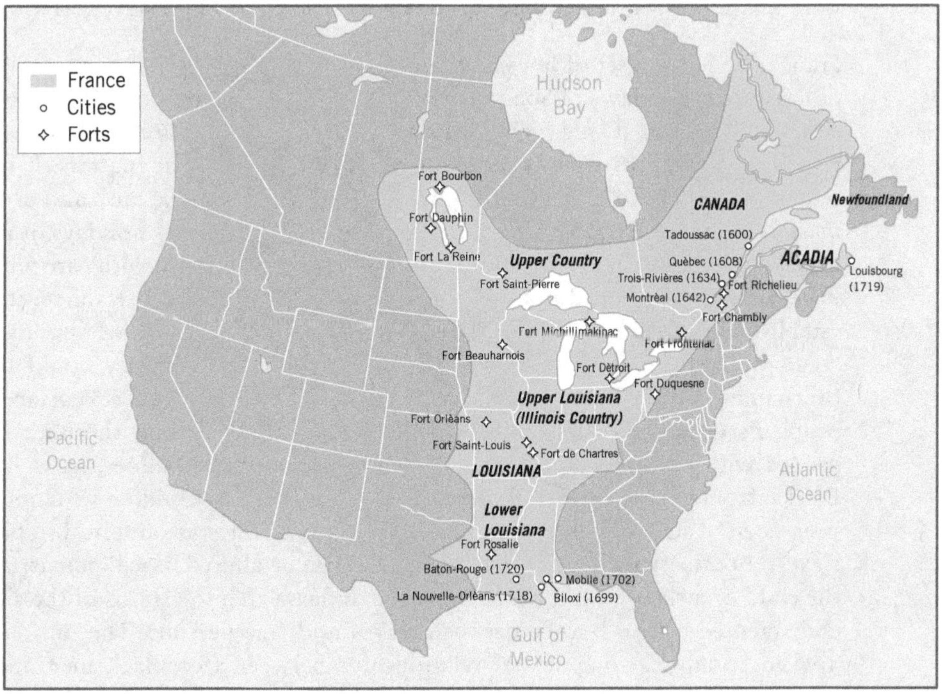

Figure 2.5 ■ France Claimed Much of the Land that Would Later Become Canada

settlements were established that this royal rhetoric was given serious consideration. The thrust of the efforts, inspired by the fur trade, provided the motivation to integrate the indigenous population into the French colonial policy, as governors and foreign missionaries were determined to save the "savages" (Belmessous 2005).

Labor Crisis and Slavery

The French, like the Spanish, soon discovered that Native American slaves could not provide sufficient labor. As the plantations and economies expanded, so did labor needs. French colonies like Louisiana encountered labor crises as they attempted to shift their economies to tobacco and sugar production. On May 1, 1689, King Louis XIV gave royal approval for the trade and use of Africans as slaves. Twenty years later, in 1709, slavery was declared legal in New France.

The first groups of imported slaves came from both France and Africa between 1717 and 1720. The group from France consisted of more than 1,400 White men and women who had been convicted as thieves and deported to New France. Riots by these French slaves caused a sudden halt to this form of slavery. Ultimately, it was Africans who filled the labor needs of New France, particularly in Louisiana. During this period close to 4,000 Africans were forcefully brought to the colony (Hall 1992). As this history demonstrates, Africans did not become slaves because they were Black; many other cultural groups were also forced into slavery (Pitts 2012).

France produced a set of laws governing slaves and Blacks that were qualitatively different from the laws of Spain. France's Colonial Ordinance of 1685, also known as the Black Code (Code Noir), legislated the life, death, purchase, marriage, and religion of slaves, as well as the treatment of slaves by their masters. It formally required all slaves to be baptized and educated in the Catholic faith and prohibited masters from forcing slaves to work on Sundays and religious holidays. It required masters to provide slaves with food, shelter, and clothing, and with care when sick. It held that slaves could not own property or have any legal recourse. It further established when they could marry, where they could be buried, what punishments could be meted out to them, and under what conditions they could be freed (Buchanan 2011). These laws were an attempt to curtail the sexual and moral problems generated by frontier society, which tended to blur the lines between groups with differing status. The Black Code prohibited Whites, as well as free Blacks, from having sexual relationships with slaves. Any children who might have been born of such unions were to become wards of the state and held in perpetual slavery. In other words, a slave's status could not be altered based on marriage, and the child of a slave would become a slave. In legalizing the status of the slave, the code created a firm border between slaves and free persons. The only loophole applied to any existing sexual relationships between free Black men and Black women who were slaves. Any children born of these unions would be rendered legitimate and free.

Left-Handed Marriages and Plaçage

Within these frontier situations, "social relations were more fluid and social hierarchies less established than they would become with the entrenchment of plantation agriculture" (Spear 2003, 90). Under these circumstances, a strange norm developed whereby men often formed alliances with Creole women in what were termed left-handed marriages. These "marriages," temporary in nature, often resulted in children who served as interpreters and mediators (Shippen 2004, 358). While such relationships were equivalent to common-law marriages, the women were not legally recognized as wives; among free people of color, these social arrangements were referred to as *plaçage*.

Plaçage flourished throughout both French and Spanish colonies. Such relationships were celebrated as part of high society in New Orleans during what became known as the city's "quadroon balls." Quadroon literally means one-quarter Black by descent. These balls provided a carnival atmosphere where elite White males could make their selections from a collection of light-skinned free women of color. A woman selected was accorded a household, typically with servants, where her status was slightly less than that of a wife and greater than that of a concubine. *Plaçage* therefore constituted a socially sanctioned form of miscegenation, or

Under the plaçage system, white men would take light skinned free women of color as their common law wives and establish them in household, often with servants.

the mixing of different racial groups, often lasting even after the man was legally married to a White woman. While technically free, the women involved in *plaçage* were both economically and socially dependent on their sexual objectification, availability, attractiveness, and ability to satisfy the fantasies of elite White men (Li 2007, 86). Eventually, the large number of free people of color and their relationships to others of mixed heritage caused the Louisiana Supreme Court to declare all such mixed-race people to be free (Hall 1992). This group had greater access to education and wealth and used both to become advocates for racial reform and freedom.

British Colonialism (1587)

After some failed attempts, the Plymouth Company's *Mayflower* finally reached the New World in 1620, where the ship's passengers established the next set of English colonies in a place they declared to be Plymouth in Massachusetts (Figure 2.6).

These settlers shared the European rationalization for imperial expansion by declaring the indigenous peoples barbaric—and saving these pagans via Christian civilization was the goal.

Building a Tradition of Slavery

The first group of non–Native Americans to wear chains in New England were poor Whites, primarily from Ireland. These slaves began arriving in New England in the early 1600s. English slave masters looked upon the Irish as backward, lazy, unscrupulous, and fit to be enslaved (Beckles 1990, 510–11). Upwards of 50,000 Irish people, mostly women and children, were forcibly deported to the Americas. Harsh treatment, hostility, and degradation led Irish and Black slaves to engage frequently in collaborative rebellions (Bernhard 1999, 89–91).

In all likelihood, the first Blacks entered Jamestown, in the colony of Virginia, in 1619 as indentured servants, but by 1661 they were legislated servants for life. In the next year, a revised statute linked slavery to maternity by declaring that all children would be free or slave according to the status of their mothers. This Virginia law was a

Figure 2.6 ■ There Were 13 Original English Colonies

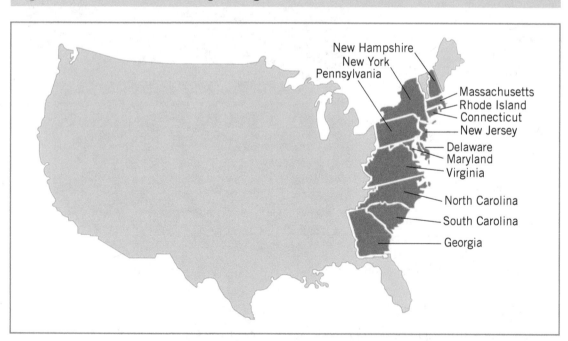

Source: U.S. Geological Survey, *National Atlas of the United States of America* (Washington, DC: U.S. Department of the Interior, 1970).

significant departure from previous British laws, which traced the status of children to their fathers. The lucrative commerce in Native American slaves commenced among the English with the founding of Carolina in 1670 and lasted through 1717. What emerged was a distinct racial hierarchy in which male European landowners dominated both Native American and African slaves (Gallay 2002). Thus, on the backs of African slaves, a racial hierarchy was constructed.

Like the Spanish and French, the English manipulated the ethnic conflicts among the various Native American groups. The English encouraged the Native Americans to avoid slavery by enslaving their adversaries and selling them to the English for trifles of cloth and beads, and, of course, guns (Gallay 2002, 6).

This new racial system finally gave birth to racial classification and defined race relations throughout the nation until the dawn of the Civil War. These new laws and new hierarchies were also motivated by attempts to divide those who otherwise might be inclined to join together in revolt.

Slave Rebellions: Voices of Resistance

Slave rebellions represented a continual and persistent source of both strain and stress for the White planter class. The response was the continual evolution of racial hierarchies buttressed by laws, sanctions, and privileges that pervaded the entire colonial social structure. Throughout this text, we will show how these resistance stories have become an integral part of Americans' national identity.

The first significant slave rebellion against the English occurred in Gloucester County, Virginia, in 1663. This conspiracy, which included both White indentured servants and slaves, aimed to overthrow the White masters. The plot was exposed by an informant, which led to the execution of several of the plotters and the passage of a series of laws that began to emphasize the ineradicable distinctions between slave masters and slaves.

Bacon's Rebellion of 1676 was the most significant challenge to the class structure (Breen 1973). The elite response to Bacon's Rebellion was to create new identities of color and race to usurp divisions of class and status. In order to understand this threat, we must understand the labor situation in 17th-century Virginia. In this revolt, Black, Irish, Scottish, and English bond servants were pitted against a small and nervous group of planter elites. Bacon, a member of displaced White labor, found himself and his group literally between a rock and a hard place. The real issue was that the increasing use of Africans as bonded labor had forced a large number of White laborers out of their positions. The irony of this is that while the members of the planter class were gaining land grants with each new allotment of workers, no such provisions were being made for those displaced by the increasing numbers of cheaper laborers.

Crop failures in 1676 provided the fuel for the violence that followed. The revolt quickly became a mass rebellion of bond servants who aimed to level the government and the entire class structure. More than 6,000 European Americans and 2,000 African Americans took up arms and fought against a tiny Anglo-American slave-owning planter class. They marched to West Point, where they took over the garrisons and military arsenal. They forced the military governor to flee and shut down all tobacco production for the next 14 months.

The rebellion threatened the very heart of the British colonial system by challenging the power of the Anglo-American slave-owning planter elite. The members of the planter class responded by solidifying slavery into a racial caste system. In the process, Whiteness was created.

Bacon's Rebellion, in Virginia in 1676, remade class and status distinctions and hardened slavery into a racial caste system.

Borderlands and Frontiers

At the time of European colonization, most of the land in the Americas was formally under the control of various Native American federations. Europeans purposefully defined these lands as frontiers or borderlands. This designation, often preserved and presented as historical fact, fails to appreciate the reality of these contested spaces (Haan 1973). Under the guise of protecting the interests of weaker states, the Europeans placed the Native Americans and their lands into "protectorate" relationships, in which the stronger European nations took on the responsibility of protectors (Haan 1973, 146). Concurrently, these same "protected" spaces became universally known as frontiers or borderlands. This designation also provided convenient camouflage for the more aggressive actions of the various European colonial systems.

These contested spaces between the Spanish, French, and English colonies provided the colonial powers with three important benefits:

- They created the illusion of Native American national sovereignty.

- They served as an outlet or safety valve for excess and displaced colonial labor and capital accumulation.

- They served as spaces where the European powers could wage imperialistic wars against each other. These wars, in which the Europeans typically encouraged or manipulated Native American tribal differences, can be viewed as proxy wars.

In this section we shall explore how frontiers and borderlands came to fulfill these functions.

The Turner Thesis—Our First Stock Story

Perhaps no single idea has so captured the American imagination, summarized and serialized the nation's official story, and misrepresented U.S. imperialistic ambitions as what is euphemistically called the Turner thesis. What makes historian Frederick J. Turner's argument so important to our narrative is that it became the dominant narrative of the United States. It represents our first stock story. Turner's basic thesis, developed in 1893, was that the American identity, which included democratic governance, rugged individualism, innovative thinking, and egalitarian viewpoints, was forged in the American frontier experience. According to Turner, the American frontier provided not only the encouragement but also the spaces to unleash the progressive spirit of freedom envisioned by various European revolutionary systems (i.e., specifically the French and English Revolutions). As significant as the Turner thesis was to the "official" narrative, it took more than 70 years for the nondominant counternarratives to be heard again. These voices told a different story, one that rejected the idea of a frontier and all of its presumptions. Rather than a blank slate of free land that was just waiting to be settled, developed, and occupied, the "frontier" was made up of sovereign lands controlled by other nations and protected by treaties. In this counternarrative, we learn of deceit and corruption, broken treaties and forgotten promises. This is the story of the frontier.

Understanding Contested Spaces

The rhetorical and political designation of the spaces between European colonies as frontiers or borderlands is central to an understanding of what and how these areas and their peoples were viewed. The crossing of frontiers and the loss of their people are typically viewed as some kind of cosmic inevitability or evolutionary truth. Such a truth positions the Native Americans as victims who passively accepted their fate. Their fate, viewed as irreversible, was that the exotic, yet inferior, native cultures would lose against the more powerful forces of civilization. While appropriately and passively sorrowful, we are left believing that these events were necessary and the natural consequences of nature, evolution, and/or civilization (Jennings 1975, 15–16). The idea of borderlands helps clarify how the three European colonial powers constructed race and space as conflicting rivalries. These conflicting rivalries not only shaped our nation but also started us on our troubled path toward a racial state (Adelman and Aron 1999, 815–16).

It is strange that our myths regarding these spaces often bring to mind such people as Daniel Boone, Davy Crockett, and James Bowie. As defenders of all

The images conjured up by the names Daniel Boone, Davy Crockett, and James Bowie—memorialized, serialized, and fantasized in both film and school curricula—capture the essence of Turner's thesis. These men are depicted as rugged individualists and noble warriors, honest and fiercely independent. And just as typically, they are juxtaposed against a prideful, ignoble, band of savages hell-bent on destruction.

that we hold dear, these men are the only forces of civilization holding back the frontier. Reality rarely lives up to such hyperbole. The Boones, Crocketts, and Bowies—as we have seen—were often displaced Whites forced into the "frontier." In this scenario, the Native Americans, defined as weak savages, are characterized as expendable and secondary to the interests of frontier survival. This feat is accomplished through the extension of the racial categories developed over time within the colonies and, by virtue of this extension, the necessity to continually extend the boundaries of civilization.

CRITICAL THINKING QUESTIONS

1. How might the racial matrix developed by the Spanish colonies have affected the racial matrices of the French and English colonial powers? What does this suggest about the social construction of race in the Americas?

2. Many institutions were created along with the American colonial systems. List some that were born during this early period.

3. What does the idea of borders as contested spaces in which race and conflict were orchestrated by European colonial elites suggest about the nature of these spaces and racial dynamics? What current events might reflect some of those same racial dynamics in the interaction of race and geography?

4. Neither Native Americans nor African slaves were passive during the colonial era, and they often worked together to challenge the racial matrix even as it was being constructed. What does this agency suggest about the racial matrix, identity, and the likelihood of change?

■ THE U.S. MATRIX AND INTERSECTIONALITY— WHERE DO WE GO FROM HERE?

In this chapter we have explored how the matrix of race and the intersecting realities of race, identities, institutions, and space are the products of European colonialism. Race is not only socially constructed, but in many ways it is also woven into the fabric of our nation. As we have examined the three original colonial roots associated with the founding of the United States, we have also seen how several of the earliest institutions—family, community, the military, the legal system, and the political system—were created within this matrix of race. In the chapters that follow we will continue to explore how race influences other major identities, such as gender, sexuality, ethnicity, and class, by examining our dominant social institutions.

Investigating Institutions and Their Narratives

In the following chapters, we will present the dominant narratives around particular social institutions in the United States. Just as the institutions of gender and race have prominent, legitimated, and powerful institutional narratives that determine bodies, identities, practices, and interactions, so too do the central institutions of social life have their own orienting stories, myths, and cultural blueprints. For instance, a dominant narrative of the institution of education is that schools are great equalizers—that education can equalize life opportunities and life chances, regardless of students' social and economic station. Similarly, the dominant narrative of American sports is that it provides a level playing field where the only factor that merits attention is an individual's talent.

Examining Intersecting Identities

It is important to gain a picture of the contemporary realities for individuals within the matrix as related to each institution. To that end, in each chapter we will provide the most recent data available—for instance, data on how Black women experience the family, on how Whites compare to Latinos within the housing sector, and on the disparities between gays and lesbians within the educational institutions of the United States. This data-rich section of each chapter will give you a glimpse into the ways in which institutional life is experienced differently depending on a person's place in the matrix, with a particular emphasis on the institution of race within each. For example, when we consider sports we identify a history of Black, Hispanic, and female athletes who have overcome both racial and gender stereotypes to dominate the sports from which they were once excluded.

Analyzing Historical Roots and Geographic Differences

Once we have established a picture of the contemporary situation faced by individuals and communities in the matrix of experience, and an understanding the nature of institutions, we can analyze the historical roots and trajectories of each. In each of the following chapters we will investigate how we as a society arrived at this contemporary moment and identify key historical moments that helped define, for instance, the shape of families and the shape of the intersectional experience within them. In our investigation of the institution of education we learn about the role of boarding schools in the cultural genocide of the indigenous communities in the United States. In contrast, we also learn about the role played by historically Black and Hispanic colleges and other institutions in helping to preserve culture and identity.

Appraising Difference, Resistance, and Transformation

Since we know that institutions construct identities, we will be looking closely at the social construction of difference within each institutional realm. How is difference constructed and utilized in the military, or in sports, or in the institution of health care? Furthermore, how do these institutions build the "perfect" soldier, athlete, or patient in order to most effectively do their work and, perhaps, in the process, support the logic of White supremacy and race? We shall repeatedly show how Blacks, Hispanics, and women have found ways to creatively engage and construct identities and cultural institutions that counteract these identities and provide integral spaces for agency. We will explore some of these sites of resistance, including the various slave rebellions and civil rights movements that have helped shape our American story.

It is important to remember that while multiple people may occupy the same position within the matrix, they still may experience it differentially. Experiences and how people perceive events are made up of a complex array of histories, geographies, and influences of family, school, friends, and other social institutions, affecting how they are viewed or remembered. People and groups are not monoliths; rather, they are varied and highly complex wholes that do not equal the sum of their parts. Thus, in the following chapters we will also pursue these variations as well as the commonalities within each institution. While institutions seem to prefer constancy, consistency, and predictability to continue doing their work, individuals and communities do not always follow suit. Both institutions and the people within them can, and often do, present new, inconsistent, and chaotic elements. For example, while Asian Americans

Boston Globe / Boston Globe / Getty Images

American sporting events, like professional football games, regularly feature the military and often allow service members to bring their families to "Military Appreciation" events.

are considered the "model minority" in the U.S. context, in schools and the institution of education, *how* this racialization is experienced varies. Similarly, we will consider who gets to have crimes and other forms of deviance excused and who gets accused—a difference that often reflects race, gender, sexuality, and class.

Following from this discussion, we will also look at a couple of key examples of social movements and collective expressions of agency aimed toward changing the way that particular institutions are experienced within the matrix. Although the logic of race has encouraged certain forms of institutionalization of the family, and schools, and the media, those who suffer from these structures often demand change, both individually and collectively. We will explore the hidden and emergent resistance stories that detail the many Black, Hispanic, Asian, and female veterans who have not only survived but also excelled in times of both war and peace.

Institutions exert a considerable amount of power within society. Most of our daily activities are governed by these institutions—it would be difficult to identify any regular activities or societal functions that are not involved in some way or another with institutions. This is equally true for groups that we identify with, such as racial, ethnic, class, and gender groups. Institutions not only regulate racial groups but also differentially reward them. In this way, institutions become the vehicles by which racial structures and processes are reproduced and the sites through which marginalized groups can transform the system.

Finally, following each chapter's critical walk-through of a central institution, we will briefly discuss the possible futures for that institution, given what we now know.

CRITICAL THINKING QUESTIONS

(We do not expect you to be able to answer these questions now, but you should consider them as you go through the rest of this volume.)

1. How does knowing that race is socially constructed inform us regarding our everyday lives? What might this suggest about how race operates? How might we change these realities?

2. Race and institutions occur both historically and geographically. How might these differences be perceived?

3. How have changes in institutions historically affected the significance or perception of race? What does this suggest about the permanence of race?

4. Agency has been and continues to be seen among various individuals and groups. What key changes have the actions of individuals and groups made in how race operates? What does this suggest regarding your ability to change these same structures?

2

KEY TERMS

Bacon's Rebellion of 1676, p. 67

Black Code, p. 64

colonialism, p. 58

frontiers, p. 68

genocide, p. 51

left-handed marriages, p. 65

miscegenation, p. 65

plaçage, p. 65

quadroon, p. 65

racial caste system, p. 61

racial violence, p. 51

settler colonies, p. 59

triple glass ceiling, p. 52

Turner thesis, p. 69

CHAPTER SUMMARY

LO 2.1 **Explore how recent events have affected how we experience race.**

The United States is a nation that has historically been defined by racial and ethnic diversity. As the U.S. population increases to an estimated 458 million by 2065, we expect immigrant births and diversity to increasingly define who we are. As much of the world, including the United States, has repeatedly been traumatized by racial and ethnic violence, our continued struggle toward equality remains a dream for some. This is especially true as we look at the triple glass ceiling and other disparities that women, especially those of color, must grapple with continuously. While Asian American women lead all other U.S. women in education, all women experience income gaps relative to White men. More than half of all Americans use online social networks and media like Facebook, and the Internet, and the racial status quo is preserved.

LO 2.2 **Describe the Americas before Columbus.**

Before Columbus sailed the seas, the continents now known as the Americas were home to millions of indigenous peoples whose cultures spanned 12,000 to 20,000 years. The first immigrants to the Americas possibly arrived on foot from Siberia and Alaska or on boats following the currents from the Pacific Islands. More than half of U.S. state names (including Michigan, Minnesota, and Missouri) reflect these rich histories, cultures, and peoples. Contrary to both myth and Hollywood, these original Americans were skilled, knowledgeable, and sophisticated, with highly advanced agricultural and animal husbandry skills, metallurgy knowledge, and a rich tradition of pottery, weaving, and textiles. Their art decorates caves and can be found in museums all over the world.

LO 2.3 **Examine the patterns of Spanish, French, and British colonialism in the Americas.**

European colonization of the Americas was most intense after the Spanish explorations of Christopher Columbus that began in 1492. Each of the major European colonial systems produced unique racial structures that ultimately blended to shape the racial fabric of the United States. Each colonial power was concerned with re-creating an image of the home country within the colonies, and each failed in its attempts. The colonizing Europeans encountered significantly different peoples with different cultural, political, and gendered systems. Their responses to these account for the variability in racial structures and the racial conflict that came to define borders and frontiers. Slave rebellions occurred in all of the colonial lands. Bacon's Rebellion of 1676 linked White and Black bond servants and almost spelled the doom of the English colonies. The racial structures that came into being in reaction to this were intended to preclude labor organizing and revolt across racial lines. In fact, Whiteness was created as a result of this rebellion. Other racial strife was associated with frontiers, or the areas that bordered the various European colonies. Three separate European colonial powers used these borderlands to extend and expand their land and power bases. The conflicting rivalries not only shaped our nation but also started us down the troubled path toward a racial state.

LO 2.4 Evaluate the intersections of race, identities, institutions, and resistance.

The matrix of race and the intersecting realities of race, identities, institutions, and space are by-products of European colonialism. All of the social institutions that followed have been infused with the matrix of race. Our goals in this text are to explore several key institutions through the lens of the matrix and the experiences of intersecting identities, and to understand how space and time have influenced both the matrix and identities across these institutions.

5

HEALTH, MEDICINE, AND HEALTH CARE

The Affordable Care Act helped many Americans get health insurance, including 8.9 million White, 4 million Hispanic, and 3 million Black adults.

CHAPTER OUTLINE

LEARNING OBJECTIVES

LO 5.1 Describe contemporary inequality in health and health care.

LO 5.2 Examine various stock narratives of inequality in health and medicine.

LO 5.3 Apply the matrix lens to the link between race and health care.

LO 5.4 Explore alternatives to the current matrix of inequality in health and medicine.

We are surrounded by health and wellness information. Our social media feeds are saturated with advice about the latest "superfoods" we should eat for optimal health, how to start and maintain an exercise regimen, and other tips to help us live longer and healthier lives. And we all know the risks involved in the various activities we engage in on a daily basis, like riding in a car, texting while driving, or crossing the street. Close to 40,000 people died in car accidents in the United States in 2016 (Korosec 2017). But how often do we consider our risk of dying because of our race or ethnicity? For those who are White, the answer is likely never. The risk of African Americans dying as the result of race-based factors is about twice as high as the risk of Americans as a whole dying from car, motorcycle, plane, train, and bicycle accidents combined. In fact, the number of race-related deaths is the "equivalent of a Boeing 767 shot out of the sky and killing everyone on board every day, 365 days a year" (Smedley, Jeffries, Adelman, and Cheng 2008, 2). And yet this issue rarely makes the headlines.

In this chapter, we will rely on the matrix framework to explore the role that health and health care narratives play in the construction of "normal" bodies and examine how the definition of normal has been used as an instrument of power and social control. We will briefly examine some key moments in the history of medicine in the United States as it pertains to race, analyze the stock stories about health and medicine and their consequences, and then shift our attention to a matrix-informed sociological approach that highlights concealed and resistance stories.

■ PATTERNS OF INEQUALITY IN HEALTH AND HEALTH CARE

Sociologists argue that examining disparities in health and mortality reveals clear evidence of the long-term effects of structural racism (Feagin and McKinney 2003). For example, researchers who investigated the impacts of both race and years of education (one indicator of class) on life expectancies found that "white U.S. men and women with 16 years or more of schooling had life expectancies far greater than black Americans with fewer than 12 years of education—14.2 years more for white men than black men, and 10.3 years more for white women than black women" (Olshansky et al. 2012, 1803). *The National Healthcare Disparities Report,* an annual report mandated by Congress, compares populations on a wide range of health and health care measures. The most recent report, on data from 2015, shows that African Americans, Hispanics, Asian Americans, and American Indians and Alaska Natives all received significantly worse health care than Whites. Similar results are found when poor populations are compared with high-income populations. Researchers have documented disparities across racial and ethnic groups in access to health care, quality of health care received, health care safety, sickness and death rates, and communication and care coordination. Nevertheless, small improvements were seen in 2015 compared to previous years. This may be linked to the implementation of the Affordable Care Act of 2010. From 2013, when ACA health insurance marketplaces began operating, to early 2016, 8.9 million White, 4 million Hispanic, and 3 million Black adults gained health insurance (Agency for Healthcare Research and Quality 2016).

African Americans, Hispanics, and American Indians and Alaska Natives all have higher rates than Whites of many of the deadliest diseases, such as stroke and type 2 diabetes (Centers for Disease Control and Prevention 2017; Spanakis and Golden 2013). Understanding health inequities and inequalities requires a nuanced examination of the range of factors involved. For example, while disease rates may be the same across racial groups, mortality rates—that is, death rates—may differ. Recent research has found that Black women are much more likely to die from breast cancer than are White women, and this gap has actually increased over the past four decades. While rates of screening have increased and treatments have improved, not all women have benefited from these advancements (Parker-Pope 2013).

Health inequities in the United States are one consequence of a long history of structural racism. As noted above, researchers have found that White men with 16 years or more of education live slightly more than 14 years longer than Black men with less than 12 years of education. At these levels of education, White women live slightly more than 13 years longer than Black women (Olshansky et al. 2012, 1803). Such racial health inequalities are significant, and while some gaps are narrowing, others are actually growing. A wide range of factors are involved, including access to care and early screenings, access to high-quality care, the nature of patient–provider relationships, class inequality, and environmental racism. To some extent, in addition to being outcomes of the long history of systemic racism in the United States, current disparities in health and health care are the results of historical events and the development of the professionalized field of medicine.

Traditional Healing

Traditional medicine consists of indigenous knowledge, skills, and practices that have been passed down over generations. Practitioners of traditional medicine use these tools to prevent and diagnose illness and disease and to improve physical, mental, and spiritual health. Many forms of traditional medicine were practiced throughout the Americas prior to colonization. One example is *curanderismo,* popular among indigenous cultures throughout Latin America and parts of the United States, and still practiced today. *Curandero/as*—traditional healers—tend to specialize in specific forms of medicine, such as midwifery, bone and muscle treatment, and herbalism. Many practitioners of traditional medicine recognize a relationship between people and nature, and may focus on healing the person rather than just the illness.

Traditional healing methods were not valued by modern medicine in the past, as medical practice became defined as the province of physicians who had graduated from medical schools (which limited admission to White men). Nevertheless, many people continued to rely on these methods, and they have played an important role in U.S. Latino culture, among other cultures.

Much of our current knowledge about the medicinal qualities of specific plants and herbs comes from traditional medicine. Researchers are finding that traditional practices continue to offer insights for modern medicine and pharmacology, yet much of this knowledge is being lost as modern practices displace traditional healing and traditional cultures around the world disappear. In the past few decades, a wide range of health professionals have shifted their focus to capturing the insights of traditional medicine. Even the World Health Organization recognizes that traditional healers are

Latina author and poet Pat Mora explores the work of Curanderas and the importance of social and cultural context: "listen to voices from the past and present, who evolve from their culture . . . definitions of illness are culture bound. We might consider it essential to stay in our comfortable homes or apartments if the soles of our feet were covered with blisters. The migrant worker, however, might sigh, apply a salve, and trudge from field to field. Illness is both a biological and social reality, and our reactions are learned" (Mora 1984, 126).

an important part of the provision of health care services in many countries, given the high respect they are usually accorded in their communities, local cultural beliefs that value them, and the very limited access many populations have to physicians and other health professionals. Traditional medicinal practices remain a widespread option around the world today, especially in rural areas and developing nations.

Modern Medicine and Discrimination

Prior to the middle of the 19th century, medicine did not exist in the United States as an organized and institutionalized discipline. Around that time, a small group of established physicians began to organize conventions designed to "defend their profession against the 'unprofessional[s]'" (Charatz-Litt 1992, 718). Facing competition from traditional healers, midwives, and self-proclaimed healers, they created the American Medical Association (AMA), a formal organization through which they would define themselves as the only authentic and legitimate practitioners of medicine.

The rise of modern medical practice in the United States was both shaped and reinforced by the broader culture of racism. Modern medicine was developed during the era of slavery, and slaves were frequently used for medical experimentation (Charatz-Litt 1992; Savitt 1982; Washington 2008). After the end of the Civil War, White doctors refused to treat Black patients, and segregation became the law. In fact, the institution of medicine played a prominent role in justifying Jim Crow laws. According to southern physicians, "Blacks were pathologically different from whites, unfit for freedom, and uneducable in the ways of better hygiene" (Charatz-Litt 1992, 719).

Denied access to White medical institutions, members of the African American community mobilized to establish their own, with assistance from White philanthropists and limited government funds. By 1900, 11 medical schools had been founded to train Black doctors. Since Black physicians were excluded from the AMA, in 1895 they created their own professional organization, the National Medical Association (NMA) (see National Medical Association, n.d.). A number of the medical schools for Black doctors did not survive, and many were shut down (Olakanmi, n.d.; Sullivan and

Excluded from the American Medical Association, Black doctors formed the National Medical Association and held annual conventions, like this one in Boston in 1909. The group, which still exists, is dedicated to promoting the interests of patients and doctors of African descent.

Mittman 2010). "Consequently, until World War II, fewer than 20 Black physicians graduated from [medical] programs each year" (Charatz-Litt 1992, 719).

Few hospitals allowed Black doctors to practice and admit patients. African Americans in the South were dramatically more likely to die due to lack of medical care than were Whites; hospitals in the South were segregated, and disproportionately fewer beds were reserved for Black patients. Black physicians and patients in the North encountered similar problems. Black patients could be admitted to only 19 of 29 hospitals in New York City, and only 3 of those allowed Black doctors to treat their patients on the premises (National Medical Association, n.d.). In 1910, life expectancy for White women was 54 years, and for White men it was 50. In stark contrast, African American women, on average, lived to age 38, and African American men to only 34 (Pollitt 1996, 401–2). The NMA was literally fighting for the lives of African Americans across the country.

The story of the NMA is an often-concealed story of resistance. From the NMA came the National Hospital Association, a lobbying arm that pushed for the right of African American doctors to treat their patients in southern hospitals. The NMA founded the *Journal of the National Medical Association,* which published not only medical research but political updates as well. The NMA continued its battles for decades, but hospitals were not desegregated until the passage of the Civil Rights Act of 1964. This very recent history still affects families today. The NMA remains an active organization, committed to addressing inequality in the medical professions and the provision of health care. We have not seen a great increase in the numbers of people of color applying to medical schools or becoming doctors. In 2014, of the total population of physicians in the United States, only about 4% were Black, and Blacks, American Indians and Alaska Natives, and Hispanics/Latinos totaled only 8.9% of all physicians (Association of American Medical Colleges 2014).

The Social Construction of "Fit" and "Unfit" Bodies

Medical institutions not only contributed to the system of White supremacy and supported legal and educational boundaries separating Blacks from Whites, but they also played a central role in racializing other groups and defining where they fell within the racial hierarchy. The stock story of race as a biological reality is one of the most significant narratives justifying health disparities by locating physical differences within the body.

Debates on how the races originated characterized the early stages of the science of race, and they were not resolved until the publication of naturalist Charles Darwin's text on the theory of evolution in 1859. Darwin asserted that all races evolved from the same organisms and thus were part of the same species (Ferber 1998). He also described a process of natural selection, in which those individuals best suited to their environments were more likely to survive and reproduce, furthering their species.

Social Darwinism and the Rise of Eugenics

Darwin's theories, and the discoveries about genetics and inheritance published by scientist and Augustinian friar Gregor Mendel in 1866, sparked a new way of thinking

The theories of Charles Darwin (left) and discoveries of Gregor Mendel focused new attention on the inheritance of traits, both physical and behavioral, and provided the basis for both social Darwinism and eugenics.

about race, class, and the value of life. This new perspective focused on the inheritance of so-called genetic traits, which were believed to include everything from physical characteristics to moral behavior.

The school of thought known as Social Darwinism took the basic insights of the theory of evolution and applied them to social life, making the assumption that a society could determine between the "fit" and "unfit." Sociologist Herbert Spencer, who coined the phrase "survival of the fittest" in 1864, argued that the imagined laws of natural selection were justification for not intervening to help the poor.

These popular versions of evolutionary theory distorted the actual science of evolution in two important ways:

1. Evolution actually works extremely slowly, over millions of years, not over the course of a few generations as assumed by proponents of social Darwinism.

2. There is no way of knowing who is or is not "fit." According to the theory of evolution, "fitness" is determined by specific historical, environmental, and climatic contexts.

That is why diversity within a species is so important to its survival in a range of contexts that cannot be predicted in advance. The fittest species is the most diverse. A diverse species is capable of surviving and adapting to a changing environment.

The eugenics movement, which arose in the late 19th century, took the social Darwinist philosophy further, arguing that natural selection should be hastened through the implementation of policies that would encourage the "fit" Northern Europeans and upper classes to reproduce; in addition, the numbers of those defined as "unfit" should be reduced through sterilization. Francis Galton, a cousin of Charles Darwin, coined the term *eugenics*. The idea was relatively simple: If evolution works by preserving the fittest, why not aid that process by eliminating some of the unfit? At the very least, social Darwinists argued, society should not be helping the unfit to survive by providing them with forms of charity and welfare. Eugenicists' arguments appealed to those of all political stripes who sought answers to the economic crisis caused by the need to care for those in society who either could not care for themselves or were considered unfit to participate in society (Ekland-Olson and Beicken 2012; Lombardo 2008). In addition to eliminating the unfit, measures were suggested to encourage the "fittest" to marry each other and reproduce in order to increase the "fit" population. This all occurred within the broader context of a system of White supremacy, so that the White race was assumed to be the "fittest" race that could continue to be perfected.

Social Darwinism and eugenics gained a broad base of support among a number of groups, including progressive organizations fighting for women's suffrage, women's right to birth control, child welfare, temperance, and prison reform. If the poor and uneducated were not competent to make educated decisions if given the vote, then it followed that those groups were most in need of limiting the numbers of births in their families and most susceptible to alcoholism, violence, and crime.

Eugenics was legitimated and given the stamp of scientific truth when the AMA included among its published goals the application of a "scientific process of selection" to control the growth of the "unfortunate classes." Ways to do this included restrictions on immigration and who could marry, and compulsory sterilization for certain people (Lombardo 2008, 11).

Eliminating the "Unfit"

Many people believed that by removing from society those incapable of living up to high moral and physical standards, they could protect the purity and fitness of the White race. These efforts went so far as to attempt to protect the sensibilities of the fit by keeping "defectives" literally out of sight. The 1911 Chicago Ugly Law declared: "Any person who is diseased, maimed, mutilated or in any way deformed so as to be an unsightly or disgusting object, or an improper person to be allowed in or on the streets, highways, thoroughfares or public places in this city shall not therein or thereon expose himself or herself to public view" (quoted in Coco 2010, 23).

Eugenic ideology permeated immigration policy as well. Beginning with the Immigration Law of 1891, the federal government classified as "public charge" certain immigrants thought likely to depend on government assistance (Park 2011, 4) Any immigrant believed to suffer from a "loathsome or dangerous contagious disease" (which included pregnancy, poverty, and a lack of morals) was deported. Women were automatically assumed to be public charge if they were unmarried or widowed.

A plethora of new methods were devised to determine who was and was not "fit," ranging from the use of tools to measure the widths and angles of the face to the first IQ tests. Some of these intelligence measures were put to use at the immigration hub at New York's Ellis Island, where scores of women trained in methods of spotting the "feebleminded" were employed to identify misfits and administer IQ tests. Those immigrants defined as "morons" were swiftly deported. In 1913, Henry Goddard, psychologist, author, and leading eugenicist, claimed that this testing showed that about 80% of Jewish, Hungarian, Italian, and Russian immigrants were feebleminded. Deportations for the reason of feeblemindedness increased 350% that year and 570% the next, a situation that played a role in the setting of immigration quotas to limit the "inferior stock" of the "not quite White."

Charles Davenport, another prominent eugenicist, focused on the elimination of what he saw as undesirable inherited traits. He meticulously sought to identify every genetic trait, publishing his documentation in 1912 in his *Trait Book*. Public education about eugenics thus increased, and public health advocates sought methods for "race improvement through better marriage" (Lombardo 2008, 45). Fears of miscegenation were also fueled by eugenic sentiment.

During this period, 33 U.S. states adopted laws allowing eugenic sterilizations in order to decrease the reproduction of undesirable genetic traits (Ekland-Olson and Beicken 2012). The traits considered undesirable were found in people of many different heritages, and the grouping of such diverse people seems arbitrary to us now; however, people with the undesirable traits were united in the public mind as deviants, as a population of defectives who deviated from the norm of the healthy racial body required for a healthy nation.

The U.S. eugenics movement achieved its greatest success in the 1927 U.S. Supreme Court case of *Buck v. Bell*. In this case, the Court upheld Virginia's law requiring sterilization of those deemed "socially inadequate" and living on government support. Eugenicists argued that Carrie Buck, a resident at the Virginia Colony for

Stephen Jay Gould (1981, 166) sharply criticizes the early 20th-century American practice of subjecting newly arrived immigrants to intelligence screenings: "Consider a group of frightened men and women who speak no English and who have just endured an oceanic voyage in steerage. Most are poor and have never gone to school; many have never held a pen or pencil in their hand. They march off the boat; one of Goddard's intuitive women takes them aside.... Could their failure be a result of testing conditions, of weakness, fear, or confusion, rather than of innate stupidity?"

Epileptics and Feebleminded who had given birth after being raped at age 16, could only produce socially inadequate offspring and was therefore a threat to both the White race and the nation (Lombardo 2008). Writing for the majority, Justice Oliver Wendell Holmes Jr. declared: "It is better for all the world, if instead of waiting to execute degenerate offspring for crime, or to let them starve for their imbecility, society can prevent those who are manifestly unfit from continuing their kind. . . . Three generations of imbeciles are enough" (quoted in Lombardo 2008, 287).

By the mid-1930s, most states had adopted laws similar to Virginia's, and more than 60,000 U.S. citizens were forcibly sterilized (Lombardo 2008). The United States was not alone in its efforts to "improve" its population; numerous other nations followed the example set by the United States and Britain, most notably Germany. Eugenic research, much of it conducted by U.S. scientists, was the foundation of Adolf Hitler's "final solution"—the elimination of the following identified categories of people: Jews, homosexuals, Romani (Gypsies), the disabled, Jehovah's Witnesses, political prisoners, habitual criminals, the asocial, and emigrants (United States Holocaust Memorial Museum, n.d.). All of these efforts revolved around the desire to "perfect" the Aryan race.

Despite widespread condemnation of Nazi practices of eugenics, in which many German doctors were complicit, the United States continued to carry out forced sterilizations in the period after World War II, with the goal of limiting the birth of "mental defectives." California led the way, sterilizing 20,000 people by 1963 (Cohen and Bonifield 2012). California's law required that anyone deemed a "ward of the state" could not be released from state custody without undergoing sterilization. Some of the victimized included teenagers who had been removed from their families because they had been neglected or abused. Between 1929 and 1974, North Carolina sterilized of more than 7,600 people, including young rape and incest victims (like Buck) who were blamed for being "promiscuous" (Snyderman 2012).

Eugenics was inherently about the construction of Whiteness, and it provides us with a clear example of the need to understand race intersectionally. Those White people who were seen as unhealthy and impure—the poor, the disabled, the homosexual, the not-quite-White Jew—were targeted for segregation or elimination. It was women's bodies, not men's, that were most often targeted for sterilization. The hierarchies of class, sexuality, ability, religion, and so on privileged the White race as the superior race.

Inventing the Homosexual

The eugenic search for hereditary "defects" or abnormalities led to efforts to locate homosexuality as something inherent in certain bodies. The invention of the homosexual—the idea that there is a homosexual body and a homosexual person (as opposed to simply sexual acts and desires)—arose in late 19th-century medical discourse. Havelock Ellis's *Studies in the Psychology of Sex* was published in 1897 and became one of the founding texts of sexology. Sexologists employed many of the same methods that race scientists used to measure or locate the bodily sources of such "defects" (Blumenfeld 2012; Somerville 2000). This resulted in members of the medical professions committing lesbians, gay males, bisexuals, and those who transgressed so-called normative gender identities and expressions (often against their will or under tremendous pressure) to hospitals, mental institutions, jails, and penitentiaries. Many were subjected to prefrontal lobotomies, electroshock, castration, and sterilization (Blumenfeld 2012).

The pathologizing of LGBT people of every race has continued since that time, with dire public health consequences. When the HIV/AIDS epidemic began in the early 1980s, gay men were among the first cases, and AIDS became known as a "gay men's disease." The false assumption that the disease was a result of individual lifestyle choices led heterosexuals to believe they were safe, and doctors to limit their study of the disease to men's symptoms only. It was more than a decade before symptoms unique to women, like cervical cancer, were recognized. By then, untold numbers of women had been misdiagnosed and denied appropriate treatment (Weber 2006, 28).

So-called conversion therapy, treatment programs meant to change the sexual orientations of gays and lesbians, remains largely legal. Although such programs are not medically oriented and are not run by doctors, in addition to being widely discredited and often harmful, they have proliferated in some states. The basis for conversion therapy is the idea that homosexuality is a mental disorder that can be cured. Some states now ban conversion therapy for minors (see Figure 5.1).

Figure 5.1 ■ Seven States Currently Ban the Practice of Conversion Therapy for Minors

Law bans conversion therapy for minors *(7 states + D.C)*
No law *(43 states)*

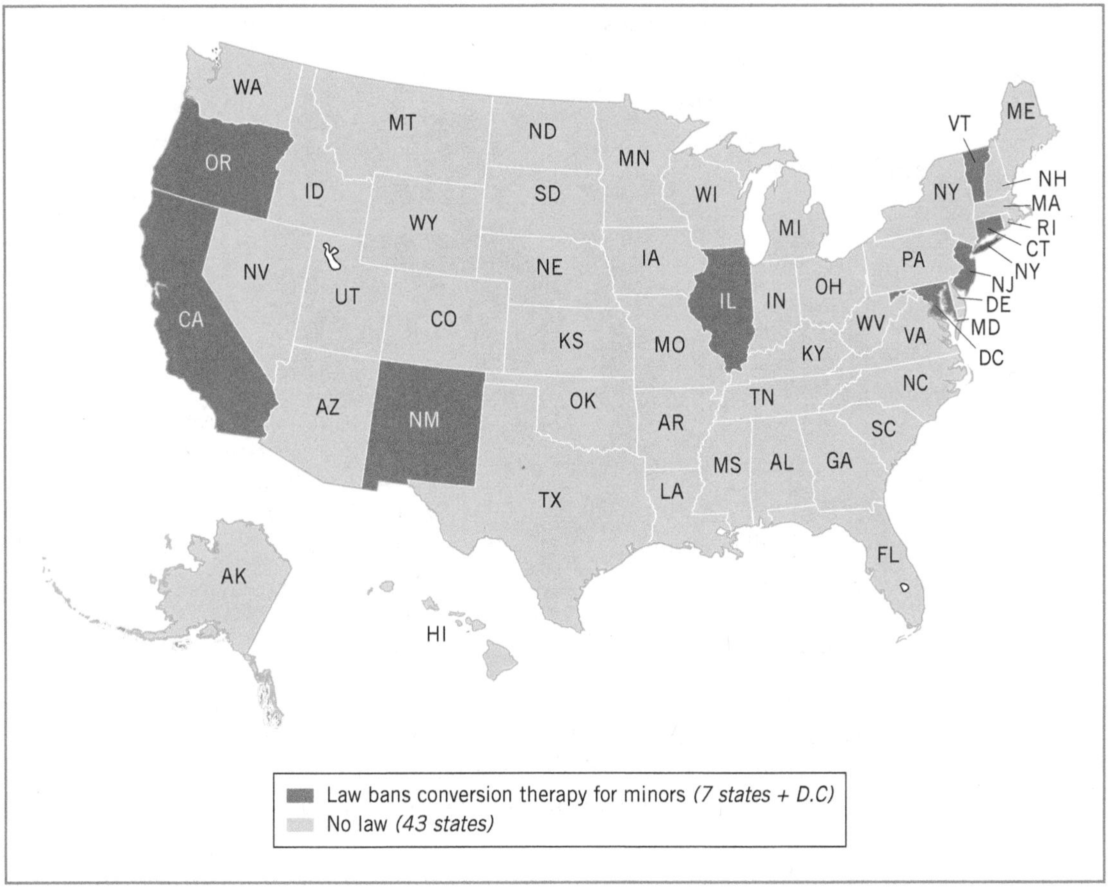

Source: Movement Advancement Project, "Conversion Therapy Laws," http://www.lgbtmap.org/equality-maps/conversion_therapy#sthash .CPvnZdAr.dpuf.
Note: These laws prohibit licensed mental health practitioners from subjecting minors to harmful "conversion therapy" practices that attempt to change their sexual orientations or gender identities. This map reflects the states that prohibit conversion therapy. In 2015, Cincinnati, Ohio, passed the first city-level conversion therapy ban.

CRITICAL THINKING

1. Historically, how have the dynamics of gender, ability, and sexuality come into play in the service of White supremacy?

2. Can you think of specific innovations in contemporary medical technology that have the potential to bring the ideas of eugenics into public debate again? What safeguards might protect people from the misguided policies of the past?

3. Can you identify any characteristics you or any of your close friends or family members possess that were targeted for elimination by eugenicists?

4. Have you or anyone you know utilized traditional medicine or "alternative" medical practices? Why do you think some of these practices are more in vogue and acceptable today, after many years of being delegitimated in the United States?

■ THEORIZING INEQUALITY IN HEALTH AND HEALTH CARE

We have witnessed tremendous change in the American health care system in our lifetimes, especially within the past few years. Patients, practitioners, and government officials are still hotly debating what the system should look like, but in the meantime, the field of medical sociology, the sociological analysis of the field and practice of medicine and their social effects, has also changed. It is only in the past half century that medical sociology has come into its own as a significant field within the discipline of sociology, and sociology courses on health and illness have become more common.

Health and illness are not simply biological phenomena—they are also social phenomena. The sociology of health and health care challenges many of our basic assumptions about illness. In this section we will examine concealed and resistance stories that challenge the predominant stock stories about health and illness, such as these:

1. Race is a biological reality that can help explain disparities in health.

2. Health is a matter of individual and genetic factors.

3. Thanks to medical advances and the elimination or minimization of many infectious diseases, people today live longer than their predecessors in previous generations.

4. The field of medicine and health care employs objective science and operates independent of the social organization of society.

In our brief historical overview, we have seen the ubiquity of the first two stock stories, and the inequalities and White privilege they have justified. We now turn to the third and fourth stories above. These assumptions may seem like common sense on the surface, but many scientists and sociologists have been building a case against these arguments for quite some time.

Historical Advances in Health and Life Expectancy

People living in industrialized Western nations live much longer today than people in previous centuries. Over the course of the 19th and 20th centuries, average life expectancy has about doubled. Until about 100 years ago, most people died from infectious diseases, such as the flu and tuberculosis. Today the leading causes of death are chronic illnesses, such as cancer, heart disease, and diabetes. What accounts for this dramatic change? While advances in medicine played a significant role, social changes made the difference for many (Braveman and Gottlieb 2014; Conrad and Leiter 2012, McKeown 2014; Rasanathan and Sharkey 2016). Throughout the 1800s, advances in knowledge regarding hygiene and nutrition were much more important in the curtailing of infectious diseases than medical interventions such as immunizations (Aiello, Larson, and Sedlak 2008a, 2008b). Research on public health has documented the pivotal role of cleaner air and water, improved sewer and sanitation systems, and increased standards of living, including better nutrition and housing.

While overall life expectancy was increasing in the Western world, gains were not consistent across race and class groups, and disparities among groups have remained fairly steady. Education levels are one factor in these gaps. White men and women with a college education or higher have been found to have life expectancies at birth that are more than a decade longer than those for Black men and women with less than a high school

Fewer African Americans experience healthy aging and longevity than members of other groups.

Education Images / Universal Images Group / Getty Images

degree. Between White and Black men with a college education or higher, the gap is approximately 5 years; when the Black men have fewer than 12 years of education, the gap is 16 years. Researchers are not hopeful about this gap narrowing in the coming years (Pollard and Scommegna 2013). German sociologist Friedrich Engels compared the life spans of the wealthy with the significantly shorter life spans of the working class, blaming social factors such as dangerous work environments and poor living conditions. In *The Philadelphia Negro,* first published in 1899, W. E. B. Du Bois examined African Americans' higher rates of disease and mortality compared with Whites. He also argued that social factors played a significant role in these disparities, blaming nonhygienic and poor living conditions and lack of protection from the elements (see Williams 2012, 283). Du Bois also identified racism itself as a variable:

> The most difficult social problem in the matter of Negro health . . . is the peculiar attitude of the nation toward the well-being of the race. There have . . . been few other cases in the history of civilized peoples where human suffering has been viewed with such peculiar indifference. (Du Bois 1899, 163, cited in Williams 2012, 287)

The Role of Objectivity in Medicine

Both conflict and functionalist schools of thought have contributed to the sociology of health and medicine. Conflict theorists argue that economic interests play the most significant role in determining health outcomes. Profit motives drive the definitions of disease, with pharmaceutical companies investing their research and development dollars in finding medications that will sell to large numbers of people, such as drugs for erectile dysfunction, rather than prioritizing their efforts based on public health needs. Economic interests also affect who is most likely to become ill, and the kind of health care they are likely to receive. Many researchers have argued that it is no coincidence that toxic waste dumps and other environmental hazards are most frequently located in or near poor communities, as we will examine later in this chapter. And because the U.S. health care system is driven by profits, the wealthy have better access to high-quality health care. Seen from this perspective, our medical system reinforces class inequality and serves as a form of social control.

Stock stories about health and health care ignore the role of institutional class and race inequity and unequal outcomes, and instead focus on the individual level and the biologized racial body. Sociologists have raised many critical questions about these assumptions and have highlighted the roles of a wide range of social factors.

1. Other than those discussed above, what additional social and economic factors influence the U.S. health care system today? Compare and contrast our system with an alternative system in another developed nation.

2. What do you see as the most important institutional factors reproducing inequities and inequalities in medicine and health care today?

3. Select a social identity not examined in this chapter, such as disability, age, or gender identity, and research the health care inequalities that exist in relation to that identity. Identify at least three inequalities.

4. Sociologists shift our focus from the individual level to the social level. Which level do you see as more dominant among physicians today? Provide an example from your own experience.

■ APPLYING THE MATRIX TO HEALTH INEQUITY AND INEQUALITY

Health care as an institution is deeply enmeshed in other social institutions. For example, when a member of a family experiences health problems, other family members are affected, and specific social patterns can be observed. When you were a child and had to stay home from school because you were ill, who stayed home with you? For most children in the United States, the answer to that question would be the child's mother or another female family member (Lam 2014). Health and medicine are also intertwined with the world of work. If you have an aging relative who needs more care than the family can provide, that care is most likely provided by women of color. The low-paying jobs of nursing assistant, home health care worker, and hospice aide are some of those in which women of color are overrepresented (Glenn 2010). Just like all other social institutions, medicine and health care are imbued with hierarchies of race, gender, class, and other axes of inequality.

The matrix perspective, which draws upon the insights of earlier approaches, raises new questions and subjects for investigation:

1. *Race is inherently social.* We have explored some of the ways health and health care are actively involved in the social construction of race, as well as the social nature of health care and medicine as social institutions that reinforce inequities based on race, class, gender, sexuality, nationality, and ability.

2. *Race is a narrative.* Discourses of health and disease serve as important stories about bodies: what kinds of bodies exist, which bodies are defined as normal and which as defective, which bodies are valued and which are not. We examine the ways in which popular ideologies about bodies and health work to naturalize hierarchies of race, gender, class and sexuality, while at the same time constructing U.S. national identity.

3. *Racial identity is relational and intersectional.* We examine some of the many ways in which the construction of race is intertwined with the construction of gendered, classed, and sexualized bodies, and the provision of health care is shaped by the intersections of race, gender, class, sexuality, and ability.

4. *Race is institutional and structural.* This chapter emphasizes the importance of the institutions of health care and medicine as sources of racial constructs and the justification of racial inequality. Further, health and health care are key sites where racism is reproduced and experienced.

5. *We are active agents in the matrix.* We highlight racialized actors as active agents, not merely acted upon by social forces but also actively involved in resisting, challenging, and shaping those social forces themselves, within specific social, historical, economic, and geographical contexts.

An Intersectional Approach to Health and Health Care

Seeing our own health as a social issue may be difficult today, given our reality-show culture, which is filled with individual stories of success and failure. Television programs like *The Biggest Loser* and *The Dr. Oz Show* encourage us to think about a health problem such as obesity as an individual problem. The current discourse around obesity and fat frames the issue as simply one of individuals making poor choices. However, both class and race are correlated with weight. Sociologists argue that overall, social factors play a greater role in health outcomes than individual factors—something that is especially important to recognize when it comes to the issue of racial disparities in health. Seeing the causes of poor health as residing within the individual reinforces the notion that racial distinctions are real and have some genetic or biological reality, leading to disparate health outcomes (Daniels and Schulz 2006). In this manner, the institution of health care reproduces the stock narrative of race as biological and inequality as a product of poor choices.

Gender and Health Care

The provision of health care is an area in which we find many cases of both oppression and resistance that require an intersectional perspective. We have already seen evidence of this in our earlier examination of the rise of modern medicine. As a result of today's longer life spans, we now face the problem of providing care for an increasingly aging population, many members of which live with severe disabilities or chronic illness. In 2016, 44 million people in the United States were providing unpaid elder care, and just as child care has historically been defined as women's responsibility, the work of home health care has also fallen on the shoulders of women. This extended workload comes at a time when most women are employed outside the home. Women who can afford to do so often leave their jobs, cut back on their work hours, or move into less demanding jobs when they take on the task of providing care to elderly relatives, losing on average approximately $324,000 they would have made in the workplace (O'Donnell 2016). And it is more common for women of color, especially African American women, to manage jobs outside the home while simultaneously caring for disabled or aging family members. For many Asian American women, the strong ideology that commitment to family trumps individual choices, such as career, can lead to a sense of obligation to care for their elders, even if it means leaving their jobs and relocating to be near their families. Women in later generations of Asian immigrant families are much more likely to feel ambivalence about this, and to feel stuck between Eastern and Western ideologies (Glenn 2010; Weng and Robinson 2014).

Home health care workers, 87% of whom are women (Health Resources and Services Administration 2015), have been excluded from the protections and benefits guaranteed to other kinds of employees through legislation, such as a minimum wage and overtime pay. In 2015, the median wage among home health care workers was $11.00 per hour (U.S. Bureau of Labor Statistics 2017). Many have historically had no health insurance themselves, although that may have changed with the implementation of the Affordable Care Act, which made access to health care available to many previously without it (access that has now become uncertain under the Trump administration). The problems these women face will only grow, because they work in a field predicted to experience some of the fastest job growth in the coming decades.

Social inequities affect the provision of health care, and consequently have impacts on income as well. Shifting our attention to health itself, in the remaining subsections we examine a sampling of the many interconnected social factors and social identities, including ethnicity, age, gender, and immigration status, that influence group health patterns in the context of historical and structural inequities.

Class and Health

The most significant element in the relationship between groups and health outcomes is the linking factor of class. Those who live in poverty experience higher rates of illness, disease, and disability, but as individual wealth increases, health improves. People in the middle class may be thrust into poverty as a result of a chronic disease or disability because of tremendous health care expenses, inadequate health insurance, and/or inability to work. Further, growing up poor has lasting consequences. Despite an adult's current class status, growing up in poverty and facing the consequences of economic adversity early in life has negative impacts on health over the life span. For example, poor nutrition in childhood affects aspects of physical development, such as height, as well as cognitive development; childhood exposure to certain environmental dangers, such as high levels of lead, also affects cognitive development; and poverty in childhood has been associated with mental health disorders such as depression and anxiety, as well as decreased ability to control anger and general response inhibition (Capistrano, Bianco, and Kim 2016; Repka 2013; Strauss and Thomas 2007).

Specific health problems are highly correlated with class and income (Syme and Berkman 2009). Class-related variables such as education, occupation, income, and wealth have all been found to influence health. A lower class status not only leads to higher mortality rates but also produces higher morbidity rates, or incidence of illness. And these trends apply not just to identifiable illnesses; they are witnessed across the spectrum of health and wellness, including in rates of mental illness. Scholars have concluded that "those in the lower classes invariably have lower life expectancy and higher death rates from all causes of death, and that this higher rate has been observed since the 12th century when data on this question were first organized" (Syme and Berkman 2009, 24).

In nearly all the rest of the world's developed countries, socialized medicine and universal health care, often free, are the norm. Yet the United States spends far more on health care than any other nation, per person and as a share of gross domestic product (even since implementation of the Affordable Care Act), as illustrated in Figure 5.2.

The ACA (the future of which is in peril) was intended to improve health care access and cut costs while providing every U.S. citizen with health care coverage. Under the law, those whose incomes are below a certain level can receive subsidies to help pay their insurance premiums, and federal funding for Medicaid has been expanded to include the very poorest in the nation. The U.S. Supreme Court has ruled, however, that states can determine for themselves whether or not to expand Medicaid, and 26 states, many of them in the South, have declined to do so. These states are home to about half the country's population, "but about 68 percent of poor, uninsured blacks and single mothers. About 60 percent of the country's uninsured working poor are in those states" (Tavernise and Gebeloff 2013). While enabling access to high-quality care remains a priority, improving access does not fully eliminate health disparities (Syme and Berkman 2009).

Almost immediately after he took office, President Trump began prompting Congress to act on his campaign promise to repeal and replace the ACA. The proposed replacement, named the American Health Care Act when it was passed by the House of Representatives in May 2017, would allow states get waivers to set aside several provisions of the ACA, as long as the waivers would enable the states to (a) lower rates, (b) increase the number of insured, or (c) advance "the public interest of the state" (Amadeo 2017).

Figure 5.2 ■ The United States Outspent Other Nations on Healthcare in 2015

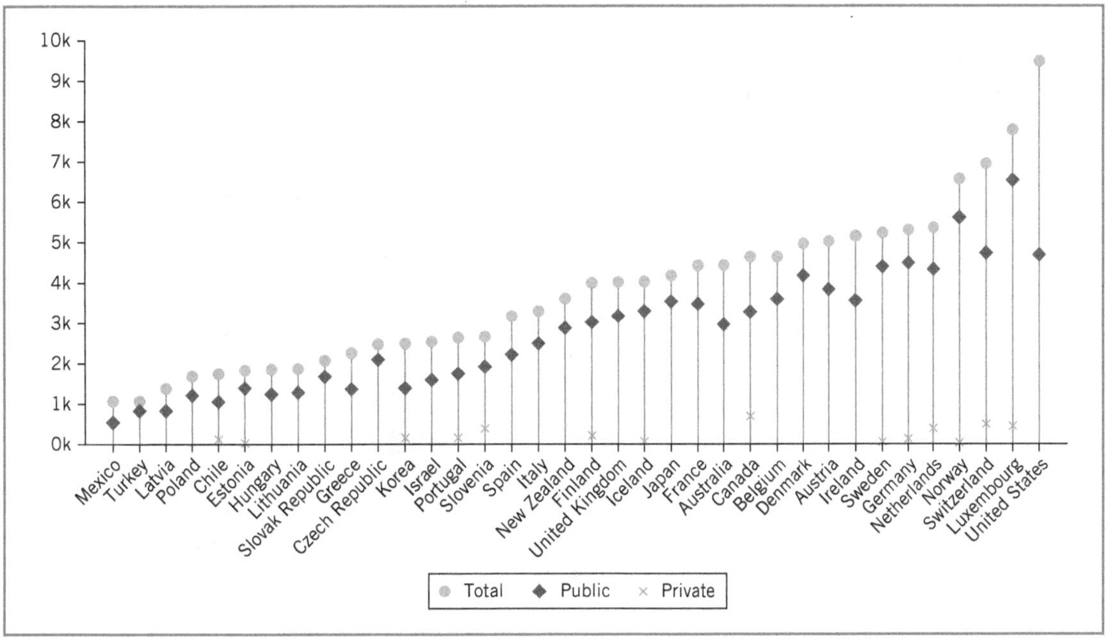

Source: Organisation for Economic Co-operation and Development, "OECD Data: Health Spending," https://data.oecd.org/healthres/health-spending.htm.

Race and Health

Because of the intersectional nature of social identities and relationships, where class dynamics are strong, we find that race is also part of the picture. The racial health gap actually increased in the 1980s as a consequence of the increasing racial income gap and widening racial inequality. While there is an overwhelming body of research documenting the impact of class on health and the interaction of class with race, the evidence also reveals that race itself is a significant factor, and sometimes a more significant factor, independent of class. For instance, depending on your race, you are more or less likely to have type 2 diabetes. Blacks, Hispanics, and Native Americans have a 50–100% higher risk than Whites of health problems and death caused by diabetes (Chow, Foster, Gonzalez, and McIver 2012). Whites experience the lowest levels of diabetes, while Native Americans face more than triple that rate. One out of three Native Americans is diabetic. Figures 5.3 and 5.4 provide a few examples of racial health disparities.

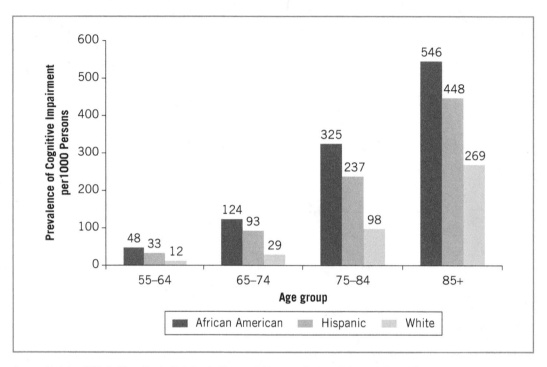

Source: Racial and Ethnic Disparities in Alzheimer's Disease: A Literature Review. February 2014. Office of the Assistant Secretary for Planning and Evaluation (ASPE), U.S. Department of Heath and Human Services.

Infants born prematurely are more likely to experience various health problems, ranging from mild to serious and chronic. Again, Whites are privileged to experience fewer preterm births, along with Asians and Pacific Islanders.

Overall, we find the greatest health inequities between Whites and African Americans and Native Americans. An "epidemiological paradox" explains the seemingly better health of Latino/as and Asian Americans. These two racialized groups are in fact heterogeneous, encompassing numerous diverse immigrant groups from different nations, with different resources, who immigrated at different points in history. When we collapse all Asians or all Latino/as into one large category, we lose sight of the differences within the group that influence health outcomes. For example, looking at infant mortality rates, Cuban Americans experience 4.7 deaths per 1,000

Source: Child Trends Databank. (2015). Preterm births. Available at: https://www.childtrends.org/?indicators=preterm-births

births, while the number for Puerto Ricans is 8.3. Combining these groups together under the label of Hispanics or Latino/as erases the inequities faced by specific ethnic subgroups (Zambrana and Dill 2006). Thus we see another of the problems inherent in relying on racial classifications.

Interestingly, the impact of immigration on health is different from what you might expect. All minority group immigrants experience significantly *better* health than their racial compatriots who are U.S.-born, including healthier birth weights, longer life expectancies, and lower rates of deadly diseases, including cancer and stroke (Ruiz, Hamann, Mehl, and O'Connor 2016; Waldstein 2010). Research has found, for example, that Mexican immigrants have much better health than U.S.-born Mexican Americans. One reason is that they experience stronger health in Mexico prior to coming to the United States. The longer they are in the United States, however, the more their health declines. Research comparing Caribbean Blacks with African Americans, and Asian immigrants with Asian Americans, has had similar findings, which also help us to understand why the health gap between Whites and others is smaller for racial groups with significant immigrant populations. These surprising findings force us to

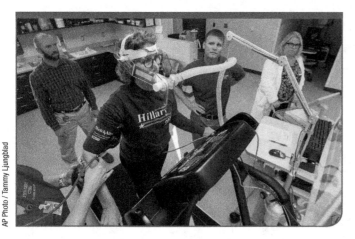

People of color are notably absent from clinical trials, in part because of this population's general mistrust of medical institutions. Other barriers to their participation in medical research include the language used in informational materials, which can be patronizing and incomplete, and the relative lack of researchers who are themselves people of color.

consider the role that simply living in the United States plays in undermining the health of people of color (De la Rosa 2002; Read and Emerson 2005; Stone and Balderrama 2008; Waldstein 2010).

Less access to and lower quality of health care can explain health inequities. Barriers to health care access are a factor in the relatively poor health of Native Americans, a group that has rarely been the focus of research on health disparities. A study examining rates of cancer among Native Americans found that, compared with Whites, Native Americans receive fewer health screenings, are diagnosed at later stages of a disease's progression, and have significantly higher cancer mortality rates. Despite the existence of early detection screening tests, Native Americans are 79% more likely than Whites to die from cervical cancer, 58% more likely to die from colorectal cancer, and 49% more likely to die from prostate cancer. Native Americans also report higher rates of dissatisfaction with the health care system (Guadagnolo et al. 2009).

African Americans face multiple barriers as well. Compared with Whites, they are less likely to have a regular location to seek health care, less likely to receive necessary medications, and more likely to experience delays in treatment. Factors like these, for example, mean that Blacks are 12% less likely than Whites to have their blood pressure under control, despite a 40% increased likelihood of having high blood pressure (National Institutes of Health 2015). Among the reasons for these kinds of outcomes are lack of access to health care, lower socioeconomic status, mistrust of providers and medical institutions, and limited health care literacy, as well as a lack of cultural competency and the continued prevalence of stereotypes among providers. Cumulatively, these factors lead to a shorter life span for African Americans compared to Whites.

Intersectional Complexity

Public health scholars Jackson and Williams (2006) have introduced the notion of an "intersectionality paradox" to describe seemingly contradictory research findings about the interactions of race, gender, and class. While very little research on health has utilized an intersectional approach, Warner and Brown (2011) have examined data showing that both African Americans and Hispanics generally suffer from higher levels of chronic disease and disability than do White people, and these researchers argue that gender also plays a role. They found that Black and Hispanic women have higher rates of chronic illness and disability than White women, and that there are greater disparities between men and women of color than between men and women who are White. In other words, the gender health gap is worse among people of color, and especially among African Americans.

Many studies also reveal that age is an interacting variable and that Black women experience the poorest health outcomes, which begin accelerating once they reach reproductive age. Warner and Brown (2011) have examined the ways in which race and gender intersect with age, looking at differences in ability/disability levels over the life course. They compared Whites, Blacks, and Mexican Americans and found that White men had the lowest disability levels, followed by White women and men of color, while Black and Hispanic women experienced the highest disability levels. They also found that these differing levels of disability increased at the same rate for each group, so the disparities remained constant over people's lifetimes. The only group for which this pattern did not hold was Black women, who experience a higher rate of disablement beginning in their reproductive years and continuing into their 60s.

Jackson and Williams (2006) also argue that to fully understand well-documented racial disparities, we must consider both class and gender. They examine the specific health inequities experienced by the Black middle class, including race-related stressors in the workplace, and find that Black middle-class men and Black middle-class women are both more vulnerable to specific sets of health problems. Recent research suggests that stress, which we examine next, is an important factor influencing health disparities.

Stress and Microaggressions

Émile Durkheim was the first sociologist to recognize the impact of stress on health (White 2009). Scholars now know that experiencing overt forms of discrimination has negative effects on both the mental and physical health of most minority group members (Sue 2010). Many studies have linked institutional racism and individual experiences of racism to poor health outcomes (Williams 2012; Sue 2010). Various studies of children and adolescents have found that youths of color report experiencing significant levels of racism, whether at school, engaged in online games and chat rooms, or elsewhere, that can be directly tied to negative mental health outcomes.

Racism and stress are key factors in explaining why some health inequities increase with age, producing a "cumulative disadvantage." Continued exposure to racism has negative impacts on the health of people of color, especially Blacks. Discrimination can lead to reduced access to desirable goods and services; internalized racism, or acceptance of society's negative characterization, can adversely affect health; racism can trigger increased exposure to traditional stressors (such as unemployment); and experiences of discrimination may constitute a neglected psychosocial stressor (Williams 2012, 284).

Similar research is being advanced in the field of psychology. First identified by Chester Pierce, founding president of the Black Psychiatrists of America, microaggressions "are brief verbal, non-verbal, and behavioral insults to a person or group, whether intentional or unintentional" (Hosokawa 2012, 21). They are a form of psychological stressor tied specifically to an individual's identity as a member of an oppressed group. The impact of microaggressions comes from their cumulative nature, and the way in which they evoke and serve as a reminder of a history of oppression. Imagine getting a paper cut. It stings for a moment and then you forget about it and move on. Now imagine getting a second paper cut, and then a third, and then a fourth—day after day, the paper cuts keep occurring. It is not long before you feel as if your whole body is cut and bleeding. That is how psychologists have described the experience of being exposed to repeated microaggressions. Those who experience a paper cut only occasionally may wonder why people of color make such a big deal of such little things, instead of brushing off a comedian's racist joke as "just kidding around," or dismissing someone's inadvertent racist comment by saying, "Hey, he made a mistake, what's the big deal?" As Sue (2010, 95) describes it: "Microaggressions are linked to a wider sociopolitical context of oppression and injustice (historical trauma) . . . [for] those who understand their own histories of discrimination and prejudice. Each small race-related slight, hurt, invalidation, insult, and indignity rubs salt into the wounds of marginalized groups in our society."

Constant exposure to microaggressions, for insance while working as a health aide in a nursing home, causes harm and creates health risks in every non-White group.

Research finds that every non-White racial group experiences harm and health risks as a result of microaggressions. As with the body's reaction to more overt stressors, the ongoing experience of microaggressions can lead to physiological responses that weaken the immune system, leaving people more vulnerable to illness and disease, including diabetes, high blood pressure, heart disease, and chronic respiratory problems (Sue 2010). The body's reaction to stress also facilitates the progression of such diseases. In a 2013 study, David H. Chae found that racial discrimination and anti-Black bias may accelerate the aging process in African American males (see Blake 2014). In addition to these physical consequences, exposure to microaggressions can threaten mental health functioning.

Those who are most affected by the stress of racism, sexism, and poverty are also least likely to have access to useful coping skills. Education, well-paying jobs, and access to health care and social services that help shore up our sense of worth and resilience are not evenly distributed in U.S. society (White 2009, 72). Women often bear the burden of supporting those who deal with stress (White 2009, 72) while at the same time taking over a greater share in caring for our aging population (Glenn 2010).

Researchers using complex statistical analyses have estimated the numbers of deaths each year due to specific social factors. They conclude that "245,000 deaths in the United States were attributable to low education, 176,000 to racial segregation, 162,000 to low social support, 133,000 to individual-level poverty, 119,000 to income inequality, and 39,000 to area-level poverty" (Galea, Tracy, Hoggatt, DiMaggio, and Karpati 2011, 1462). Yet no single factor explains all health inequities. Thinking about the visual image of how each individual is situated within the matrix, we have seen that within the institution of health care, a wide range of social identities and social factors, all of which are context specific (shaped by history and place), play important roles. But despite widespread understanding that social factors are some of the most significant influences on health, some scholars continue to seek answers in our biology.

A Legacy of Mistrust

One of the important concealed narratives that sociologists have identified is that medical theories determine the questions for study, framing them as scientific "problems" to be solved and guiding the possible answers, thus limiting what is even imaginable. This process has consequences. People defined as suffering from specific maladies can become subject to various medical, political, and legal forms of social control. Consider the case of drapetomania, a "mental illness" invented to explain why slaves tried to escape slavery.

Described by Samuel Cartwright in his book *Diseases and Peculiarities of the Negro Race* (1851), this disease could exist only in the context of a White supremacist society that sees slavery as the natural role for human beings defined as inferior. Slavery's stock story posited that slaves were happy to be slaves and were in their natural place according to God's plan. However, if they were happy and content as slaves, and slavery was God's will, what could explain the many cases of runaways? Drapetomania was the answer, and it also provided a cure—the amputation of the big toes. This remedy was successful because it physically prevented the slave from running away again. The case of drapetomania "was both a product of that society and helped to reinforce the power relations of that society" (White 2009, 43).

Mistrust of medicine is frequently a barrier for people of color. As one man put it, "I think that most of the people who are in control of research don't look like me, and I don't have confidence in how they perceive my value and my worth. I would be very reluctant to give anybody a blank check with respect to experimenting with my body and my life, my health" (quoted in Freimuth et al. 2001, 806). Given the history of medical experimentation, such mistrust is certainly understandable.

Perhaps the best-known medical experiment on a U.S. minority group is the Tuskegee Study of Untreated Syphilis in the Negro Male. This study, conducted from 1932 to 1972, is still the longest-running nontherapeutic medical study in U.S. history. Nearly 400 African American men with syphilis were recruited as subjects in Macon County, Alabama, by the U.S. Public Health Service, in collaboration with Tuskegee University, a historically Black institution. The men in the experimental group were never informed that they had syphilis, even as the study followed the natural progression of the disease and the study's doctors withheld treatment options such as penicillin, which became the standard of care for syphilis during the study period. It is estimated that between 28 and 100 of the 400 infected men died as a result of their untreated syphilis.

The narrative of this study (which was finally ended after a whistle-blower went to the press) helps explain why many Black people harbor fears and mistrust when it comes to the medical research establishment (Alsan and Wanamaker 2016; Boulware, Cooper, Ratner, LaVeist, and Powe 2003; Brenick, Romano, Kegler, and Eaton 2017; Thomas and Quinn 1991), Researchers argue that this history, combined with the cultural meanings of disease, has created a climate in which fears undermine public health efforts, such as those targeting AIDS in the African American community and many others (Thomas and Quinn 1991). Alsan and Wanamaker (2016) found that public news of the Tuskegee study in 1972 was directly correlated with a decline in Black men's trust of the medical establishment and visits to physicians, and with an increase in morbidity rates. Most significant, the researchers found a 1.4-year decrease in life expectancy among Black men over 45 years old.

The Role of Place and Environmental Racism

Where we live also affects our health, and segregated housing is a significant factor in health inequality. In 1899, W. E. B. Du Bois observed that poor people of color and poor Whites faced different living conditions that had impacts on their health. High levels of residential racial segregation persist in the United States, and people of color are more likely than Whites to be segregated in neighborhoods that are isolated from key social services and have poor living conditions, including environmental threats to health (Schulz et al. 2016). Poor Whites are more likely than poor people of color to live in economically diverse neighborhoods, with greater access to resources. As Williams (2012, 284) has reported, "In 100 of America's largest metropolitan areas, 75 percent of all African American children and 69 percent of all Latino children are growing up in more negative residential environments than are the worst-off white children." Neighborhood racial segregation also raises the risk of low birth weight beyond what would be expected from only economic differences (Debbink and Bader 2011; Gray, Edwards, Schultz, and Miranda 2014).

Environmental Risks

Race and class are both linked to exposure to environmental health risks. Hazardous waste dumps, landfills, incinerators, and other toxic sites are much more likely to be located in poor and minority neighborhoods than in wealthier, Whiter ones. People residing in neighborhoods that are primarily minority and lower-class are also exposed to higher levels of pollution, asbestos, and lead, and any playgrounds in these neighborhoods are usually older and unsafe (Massey 2004). A large body of research documents these realities and their impacts. For example, people of color and low-income Whites are significantly more likely to suffer from asthma, a difference that begins early in childhood. Research in California found that Whites are half as likely as people of color to live in areas where they face high cancer risks due to toxins in the air. Children of color face greater levels of pollution and lead poisoning at their schools, during a key period of development. Exposure to high levels of pollution contributes to lower academic performance, and lead poisoning produces permanent behavioral and neurological changes, including decreased IQ, as well as organ damage and even death (Agency for Toxic Substances and Disease Registry 2000).

Epidemiology

Social epidemiologists and sociologists are helping us to understand how race, class, and health are linked. Employing an "ecological perspective in health research" also adds to our understanding of these complex phenomena (McLaren and Hawe 2005). Public health specialists are currently showing a growing interest in this approach. *Ecological* is defined broadly here to include the entire context: all of the levels depicted in the matrix visual—history, place (both local and global), identity, the individual, and

Minority and poor neighborhoods are more likely to be near sources of exposure to toxins and environmental pollutants. Minority children are more likely to suffer from asthma and lead exposure as a result.

Chip Chipman/Bloomberg/Getty Images

so on (McLaren and Hawe 2005). These various theoretical perspectives acknowledge the importance of social structures and organizations, and culture and narratives of inequality, which all contribute to health disparities.

Epidemiology is the study of "the distribution of health issues (diseases or injuries) and health determinants in a population" (Conrad and Leiter 2012, 24). Epidemiologists focus on populations, rather than on individuals, to explain why some groups may be more likely to develop specific diseases; they look at factors such as the characteristics of the social groups themselves, the areas in which they live, and the environmental elements to which they are exposed.

The Human Genome Project

Today, research on race and genetics is progressing at a faster rate than ever before. In 1990, the internationally funded Human Genome Project (HGP) set out to map and sequence the entire spectrum of human genes. Recalling Davenport's attempt to create a comprehensive catalog of every human trait, sociologist Troy Duster (2003) refers to these contemporary efforts as a "backdoor to eugenics."

The HGP, which was completed in 2003, sparked renewed debate over the use of race in medicine and science. While geneticists acknowledge that race has no genetic basis, there is disagreement about the usefulness of race as a system of categories for sorting human differences. Some geneticists and biomedical researchers argue that our taken-for-granted racial classifications can be used as a means of dividing people into groups based on shared ancestry (Ossorio and Duster 2005, 117). However, scientists have discovered that approximately 85% of human genetic variation occurs *within* so-called races—far more than can be found between any racialized groups. People categorized as belonging to the same race may have very little in common genetically or biologically (Ossorio and Duster 2005, 117).

This view of genetic variation would seem to make racial categorizations useless. However, there are other interests at stake. One purpose of the HGP was to identify genetic markers for susceptibility to specific genetic disorders, so that gene therapies could be developed to prevent, treat, or cure them. According to the U.S. government's Human Genome Project website, "An important feature of the HGP project was the federal government's long-standing dedication to the transfer of technology to the private sector. By licensing technologies to private companies and awarding grants for innovative research, the project catalyzed the multibillion-dollar U.S. biotechnology industry and fostered the development of new medical applications." The website boasts that as a result of the HGP, many wide-ranging industries are booming, and "new entrepreneurs" are popping up to "offer an abundance of genomic services and applications" (Human Genome Project Information Archive 2013).

We have seen the growth of companies offering to provide us with information about our ancestors; the birth of the first racially targeted medicine, BiDil, a heart disease drug marketed to African Americans; and new methods of screening for birth "defects" and genetic diseases. While some of these advances may be welcome, they also carry unexamined assumptions from our eugenic past. For example, disability activists warn that screening for birth "defects" once again defines disabled bodies as "unfit" and as potential targets for elimination (Saxton 2010).

These developments also target individual consumers. The individualization of health and medicine directs our attention away from the larger issue of racial inequities in health and the factors that produce those inequities, supporting the stock story that locates inferiority in the bodies of people of color (Daniels and Schulz 2006; Hubbard and Wald 1999). Scholar Emily Martin (2006, 86) addresses the ethical dilemma raised by this approach in her critique of drugs tailored to specific racial groups. She asks, "Will making more and better medicines available to African Americans who suffer more stress due to poverty and racism provide something we want to call a solution, let alone a cure?"

Sociologists Ossorio and Duster (2005, 116) offer a way out of the trap of seeing race as either useful or not. They suggest an alternative perspective, informed by a sociological lens:

> Race and racial categories can best be understood as a set of social processes that can create biological consequences; race is a set of social processes with biological feedbacks that require empirical investigation. Researchers ought to be discussing when and how best to use race as a variable rather than arguing about the categorical exclusion or inclusion of race in science. Researchers ought to interrogate the meaning of observed racial differences. In doing so, they must recognize that race may be a consequence of differential treatment and experiences rather than an independent cause of differential outcomes.

One of the foundational arguments of a sociological perspective on health and medicine is that scientific knowledge is an inherently social enterprise (White 2009, 14). The scientific-medical eugenics discourse was the product of a specific social and historical context, and reflected the values of the dominant members of society. While some scholars refer to eugenics as pseudoscience, we have chosen not to do so, but to instead emphasize the fact that *all* scientific and medical knowledge is social. Eugenics is not a unique example of how medicine can be penetrated by social prejudices. Instead, medicine is always a social practice. It is carried out by social beings in specific social and cultural contexts.

CRITICAL THINKING

1. How has the tendency to focus on genetics changed over time? What do you see as possible positive and negative outcomes of the Human Genome Project and today's renewed interest in genetics as they shape both health and identity?

2. How do social factors pervade the institution of health care and medicine, resulting in differential health outcomes?

3. What motivations may underlie drug companies' efforts to develop race-specific medications?

4. How might your own intersecting identities shape your physical and mental health?

■ RESISTING AND TRANSFORMING INEQUALITY IN HEALTH AND HEALTH CARE

The title of Sandra Morgen's 2002 book about the women's health movement, *Into Our Own Hands,* is an apt description of the steps taken by every community of color in the United States. In response to a long history of systemic racist violence, abuse, and neglect, we find remarkable numbers of individuals and communities facing these challenges head-on and working to meet their own health needs while simultaneously battling racist institutions and organizations. We have already seen one example in the history of the National Medical Association. Below we examine a few more.

Urban American Indian Health Care

Overall, people of color are more likely than their White counterparts to receive low-quality health care. Native Americans, however, face some unique circumstances. More than 560 tribes are currently recognized by the U.S. government and entitled to specific health care benefits. However, to receive those benefits, an individual must also be legally recognized, through a bureaucratic process, as a member of one of those tribes. Health care services provided by the Indian Health Service (IHS), a division of the U.S. Department of Health and Human Services established in 1955, are reserved for members of recognized tribes, generally provided on reservations, and concentrated in areas with the largest Indian populations. This means that some tribes benefit more than others (Fixico 2000). Where available, however, IHS-provided health care is free and likely to be culturally responsive and respectful of indigenous traditions. Despite some successes, however, the health disparities between Native Americans and Whites remain wide (Indian Health Service 2017).

About 70% of American Indians and Alaska Natives have moved away from reservations to urban areas, where obtaining health care is more difficult and expensive, and the care available is less culturally sensitive. According to the Urban Indian Health Commission (2007, 1), "Today's urban Indians are mostly the product of failed federal government policies that facilitated the urbanization of Indians, and the lack of sufficient aid to assure success with this transition has placed them at greater health risk." One example of this increased risk is the suicide rate among urban American Indian youth, which is 62% higher than the national average. In addition to the factors noted above, urban American Indians have few informal and formal community support networks to turn to for support, and they are unlikely to find traditional or even American Indian health care providers (Burrage, Gone, and Momper 2016; Filippi et al. 2016).

Comparatively little information is available on the specific health risks and needs facing American Indians and Alaska Natives, and even less is known about the health risks and needs of urban Native Americans. What research does exist provides evidence that Native Americans face disproportionate levels of depression and other mental health issues, type 2 diabetes, and poor cardiovascular health. Many also experience symptoms of, and are more likely to die from, these diseases at earlier ages. For example, compared to the U.S. population as a whole, Native Americans are more than three times as likely to die from diabetes-related strokes. The infant mortality rate for Native Americans is 33% higher than that for Whites, and their rate of deaths related to alcohol is 178% higher. Further, the majority of the nonelderly Native American population has been classified as either poor or near-poor, and while 25% qualify for Medicaid, only 17% report they are receiving benefits (Urban Indian Health Commission 2007).

In response to these circumstances, Native Americans have founded many urban health organizations to provide prevention and treatment services in culturally appropriate and respectful ways. These organizations have also been making efforts to improve data collection and research on this community, although limited funding has curtailed this work, which has yet to achieve its full potential. While these organizations can produce some measure of improvement at the individual and local levels, they argue that the Native American community faces issues that cannot be remedied without broader structural changes that address federal policy, including but not limited to the provision of health services, as well as socioeconomic factors. The history of extermination, segregation, broken promises, and recent patterns of government neglect will not be remedied by individual-level responses.

Race, Reproduction, and the Women's Health Movement

The first wave of the women's movement, besides fighting for suffrage in the early 20th century, also focused on access to birth control. At the time, any public discussion of contraception was against the law, which limited information access to well-off women who could consult with private doctors. Margaret Sanger, one of the leaders of the birth control movement, was arrested for promoting contraception through the U.S. mail. Again arrested and jailed for opening the first birth control clinic in 1916, she founded the American Birth Control League, which later became Planned Parenthood. Keenly aware of the barriers faced by immigrant women, Sanger used the racism and eugenics ideology of the time to argue that birth control would benefit White society by limiting the numbers of children born to immigrant families from Southern and Eastern Europe (DuBois and Dumenil 2012). Immigrant women would beg Sanger, who worked as a nurse, for information on how to prevent pregnancy, and she witnessed firsthand the poor health and needless deaths of many married women due to too many pregnancies.

Because of the racist inflection of the debate over birth control, and its connections with the eugenics movement, Black women sought to educate themselves about birth control and reproductive health, beginning with the women's clubs affiliated with the National Association of Colored Women. For Black women, as for many other marginalized women, the issue of reproductive rights included not only the right to use contraception but also the rights to choose to have children and to be free of nonconsensual sterilization.

Women's educational and occupational opportunities are limited if they have no control over their reproduction. Further, their economic dependence on men is reinforced and solidified when they have large numbers of children to care for. Growing directly out of the second wave of the women's rights movement, the women's health movement in the late 1960s and early 1970s particularly focused on increasing women's control over their reproductive and sexual health. Early on, women of color like Byllye Avery became "acutely aware of how little information existed about Black women's health and of how the movement [they were] part of defined issues, strategies, and services with little attention or awareness of the specific needs and perspectives of women of color" (Morgen 2002, 41). The mainstream women's movement's narrow focus on abortion and choice needed to be expanded to encompass the fuller range of women's reproductive needs and rights.

Avery, a board member of the National Women's Health Network, worked with others to form self-help groups for Black women, and initiated the NWHN's National Black Women's Health Project (NBWHP), which became its own organization in 1984. The NBWHP situated Black women's health within the larger context of not only sexism but also racism and class inequality, and broadened its focus from the "pro-choice" platform to one of reproductive justice, defined as "the right to have children, not have children, and to parent the children we have in safe and healthy environments. Reproductive justice addresses the social reality of inequality, specifically, the inequality of opportunities that we have to control our reproductive destiny" (SisterSong 2013). For example, when the NBWHP started the Center for Black Women's Wellness in Atlanta, alongside the many medical

Loretta Ross—Not Just Choice but Reproductive Justice

I was born in 1953 in Temple, Texas, the sixth of eight children in a churchgoing family. I was raped by a soldier at the age of 11 and then again by my mother's adult cousin. At age 16, I had an abortion. My mother would not consent to my obtaining birth control, although I was already a teen mother and attending my first year of college thousands of miles away from home. I was lucky—abortion had been legalized in Washington, D.C., in 1970, the year I desperately needed one, so I avoided the back alley. I had a safe and legal abortion, although my older sister had to forge my mother's signature on the consent form. I do not, in any way, regret my decision. What happened to me—rape, incest, parental blocking—should not happen to any other girl, and I'm proud to be a feminist fighting for all women's human rights. African American women have made consistent and critical activist contributions to the evolution of the reproductive rights movement in the United States, expanding the movement to highlight other aspects of our struggle to achieve reproductive freedom based on our experiences of pregnancy, infant mortality, sterilization abuse, welfare abuse, and sexuality in general.

I began my work as a reproductive justice activist in the early 1970s, focusing on sterilization abuse. I have witnessed the development of a strong reproductive freedom movement among Black women during this period. In doing research to support my activism, I discovered a long tradition of reproductive rights advocacy by Black women that was either undocumented or not widely understood. I became determined to reconnect the work of Black activists at the beginning of the 20th century to the work and ideology of those at the century's end.

I have spent 38 years launching and managing nonprofit feminist organizations, including SisterSong Women of Color Reproductive Justice Collective. The Collective was formed in 1997 to fulfill a need for a national movement by women of color to organize our voices to represent ourselves and our communities. SisterSong comprises 80 local, regional, and national grassroots organizations. SisterSong educates women of color on reproductive and sexual health and rights, and works toward improving access to health services, information, and resources that are culturally and linguistically appropriate through the integration of the disciplines of community organizing, self-help, and human rights education. The mission of SisterSong is to amplify and strengthen the collective voices of indigenous women and women of color to ensure reproductive justice through securing human rights.

Joining the women's movement not only transformed my life but also saved it. On my journey, I've learned about women's human rights, reproductive justice, White supremacy, and women of color organizing.

services the center provided, "vocational and educational training" were also offered (Morgen 2002, 49).

The conferences, workshops, and other activities of the NBWHP nurtured other new grassroots organizations in the 1980s, including the National Latina Health Organization, the Native American Women's Health Education Resource Center, and the National Asian Women's Health Organization. Each of these organizations maintains an emphasis on the diversity of women's needs within these communities, while at the same time addressing some of the specific challenges each constituent group faces.

Today, a vibrant movement is fighting for reproductive justice. Women with disabilities have embraced and advanced the reproductive justice framework based on their own history of sterilization, the treatment of people with disabilities as nonsexual beings, the risks posed by genetic testing that attempts to eliminate the disabled, and more. A reproductive justice approach moves disability rights activism from a focus on individual rights to a framework that examines access to services and support that can allow society to acknowledge the inherent value and worth of human beings with disabilities (Jesudason and Epstein 2011). While *Roe v. Wade* (1972) declared women's right to control their reproductive systems, restrictions limiting this right have proliferated. As of April 2016, 43 states had laws restricting access to abortion (https://www.guttmacher.org/). In 87% of U.S. counties, women have no access to an abortion provider.

The efforts of international nongovernmental organizations supporting women's health have also increased over the past few decades, while U.S. aid has declined. While reproductive health inequities reflect existing social and economic inequities, they also reinforce them. International family planning programs are one key component of improving women's lives around the world (Sedgh, Hussain, Bankole, and Singh 2007, 5). In developing nations, researchers have found that more than one in seven married women needs or wants contraception, but is not using any. The same is true for one in thirteen women ages 15 to 29 who have never married. The most common reason these women are not using contraception is a lack of access to "supplies and services," including counseling and education about contraceptive options (Sedgh et al. 2007, 5). Around the world, women are working together locally to improve women's health. In order to improve health and health care access among oppressed populations, those directly affected must be a part of the process of finding solutions.

A Path to the Future

One of the most important lessons we can learn from the many health care movements run by and for marginalized women is that strategies that narrowly target access and individual behavior are not enough. Health inequities are a social problem that requires much broader social change.

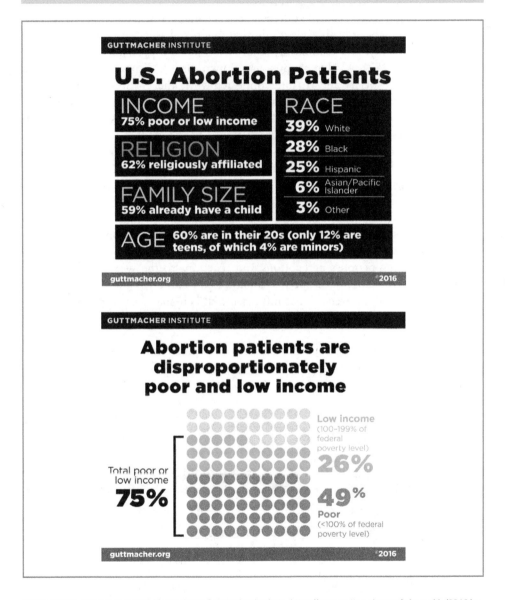

Sources: "U.S. Abortion Patients" May 9, 2016, Guttmacher Institute, https://www.guttmacher.org/infographic/2016/us-abortion-patients.

"Abortion patients are disproportionately poor and low income," May 9, 2016, Guttmacher Institute, https://www.guttmacher.org/infographic/2016/abortion-patients-are-disproportionately-poor-and-low-income.

Evidence suggests that policies targeting inequality at a broader level can reduce the health gap. For example, in the United States, states with higher levels of social spending have higher overall levels of health (Gallet and Doucouliagos 2017; Verma, Clark, Leider, and Bishai 2016). Perhaps not surprisingly, research on the views that U.S. citizens hold about health has found that few people see "employment, education, housing quality, and community safety as important determinants of health" (Williams 2012, 287). As this chapter has shown, health disparities reflect social inequalities in our society and are interconnected with other institutional structures, such as economy, education, the law, and a culture that reproduces racial inequality (Weber 2006). Simplistic individual-level responses, like telling someone to lose weight, will not solve the deep-rooted problems of health inequities. The good news is that institutions of medicine are taking a crucial first step in acknowledging the importance of social factors. In 2015, the Association of American Medical Colleges began requiring students taking the MCAT entrance exam to have background knowledge in the social sciences. As the association announced in 2012:

> A new section, "Psychological, Social, and Biological Foundations of Behavior," will test the ways in which these areas influence a variety of factors, including people's perceptions and reactions to the world; behavior and behavior change; what people think about themselves and others; cultural and social differences that influence well-being; and the relationships among socio-economic factors, access to resources, and well-being.

A truly interdisciplinary approach is essential to a real commitment to decreasing health inequities.

KEY TERMS

American Medical Association, p. 160

conversion therapy, p. 167

curandero/as, p. 159

drapetomania, p. 181

epidemiology, p. 184

eugenics, p. 163

Human Genome Project, p. 184

internalized racism, p. 179

medical sociology, p. 168

microaggressions, p. 180

morbidity rates, p. 174

mortality rates, p. 158

reproductive justice, p. 188

Social Darwinism, p. 163

traditional medicine, p. 159

LO 5.1 Describe contemporary inequality in health and health care.

Today's disparities among racial and ethnic groups in health and mortality are evidence of the historical and ongoing effects of structural racism. Racial disparities exist in health care access, disease prevention, identification of disease, treatment, care coordination, outcomes, patient satisfaction, and more. Today's health disparities have been significantly shaped by historical patterns of White privilege and White supremacy. Modern medicine displaced traditional methods of healing in many cultures, and played a central role in the construction of racial classifications and corresponding notions of difference. History is replete with examples of resistance to health inequities. African Americans developed their own health care systems in response to their exclusion from segregated institutions.

LO 5.2 Examine various stock narratives of inequality in health and medicine.

Our stock stories lead us to assume that medical advances are responsible for today's longer life spans; that the field of medicine and health care employs objective science; that race is a biological reality that can help explain disparities in health; and that health is strictly a matter of individual and genetic factors. Research, however, reveals the important roles of social factors such as hygiene and nutrition, as well as race and class.

LO 5.3 Apply the matrix lens to the link between race and health care.

The matrix perspective highlights various social factors contributing to racial health inequity and inequality, including stress, social relationships, socioeconomic factors, residential segregation, environmental factors, and mistrust, as well as the interactions of race, class, gender, age, and more. The field of social epidemiology highlights the relationships among race, class, and health, and explains the "epidemiological paradox" of better *overall* health among Asians and Latinos, racial groups with significant numbers of immigrants.

LO 5.4 Explore alternatives to the current matrix of inequality in health and medicine.

Disenfranchised groups have created many organizations to address and act as advocates for their health needs. Urban Indian health organizations and a wide array of health organizations founded by women of color place these groups' health needs within the broader context of social and institutional factors shaped by a history of racism. These organizations argue that health disparities cannot be remedied without broader structural changes. Organizations started and run by women of color and disabled women have fought for a more inclusive understanding of women's reproductive health needs.

■ CHAPTER 1

Adams, Maurianne, Lee Anne Bell, and Pat Griffin, eds. 1997. *Teaching for Diversity and Social Justice: A Sourcebook.* New York: Routledge.

African American Policy Forum. 2009. "A Primer on Intersectionality." Accessed April 7, 2017. http://static .squarespace.com/static/53f2 0d90e4b0b80451158d8c/53 f399a5e4b029c2ffbe26c c/53f399c8e4b029c2ffbe 2b28/1408473544947/598 19079-Intersectionality-Primer .pdf?format=original.

Almeida, Rhea, Pilar Hernández-Wolfe, and Carolyn Tubbs. 2011. "Cultural Equity: Bridging the Complexity of Social Identities with Therapeutic Practices." *International Journal of Narrative Therapy and Community Work* 3: 43–56.

Anderson, Monica. 2017. "African Immigrant Population in U.S. Steadily Climbs." Fact Tank, Pew Research Center, February 14. Accessed April 7, 2017. http://www .pewresearch.org/fact-tank/2017/02/14/african-immigrant-population-in-u-s-steadily-climbs.

Anzaldúa, Gloria. 2007. *Borderlands/La Frontera: The New Mestiza.* 3rd ed. San Francisco: Aunt Lute Books.

Barnett, Bernice McNair. 1995. "Black Women's Collectivist Movement Organizations: Their Struggles during the 'Doldrums.'" In *Feminist Organizations: Harvest of the New Women's Movement,* edited by Myra Marx Ferree and Patricia Yancey Martin. Philadelphia: Temple University Press.

Barzun, Jacques. (1937) 1965. *Race: A Study in Superstition.* New York: Harper.

Battiste, Marie. 2002. "Indigenous Knowledge and Pedagogy in First Nations Education: A Literature Review with Recommendations." Paper prepared for the National Working Group on Education and the Minister of Indian Affairs, Indian and Northern Affairs Canada. Accessed July 19, 2011. http:// www.afn.ca/uploads/files/ education/24._2002_oct_ marie_battiste_ indigenousknowledge andpedagogy_lit_review_for_ min_working_group.pdf

Baunach, Dawn Michelle. 2012. "Changing Same-Sex Marriage Attitudes in America from 1988 through 2010." *Public Opinion Quarterly* 76, no. 2: 364–78.

Bell, Lee Anne. 2010. *Storytelling for Social Justice: Connecting Narrative and the Arts in Antiracist Teaching.* New York: Routledge.

Bonilla-Silva, Eduardo. 2003. "'New Racism,' Color-Blind Racism, and the Future of Whiteness in America." In *White Out: The Continuing Significance of Race,* edited by Ashley W. Doane and Eduardo Bonilla-Silva. New York: Routledge.

——. 2010. *Racism without Racists: Color-Blind Racism and the Persistence of Racial Inequality in the United States.* 3rd ed. Lanham, MD: Rowman & Littlefield.

Brandt-Rauf, P. W., and S. I. Brandt-Rauf. 1987. "History of Occupational Medicine: Relevance of Imhotep and the Edwin Smith Papyrus." *British Journal of Industrial Medicine* 44: 68–70.

Brodkin, Karen. 1998. *How Jews Became White Folks and What That Says about Race in America.* New Brunswick, NJ: Rutgers University Press.

Brown, Catrina, and Tod Augusta-Scott, eds. 2007. *Narrative Therapy: Making Meaning, Making Lives.* Thousand Oaks, CA: Sage.

Bush, Melanie E. L. 2011. *Everyday Forms of Whiteness: Understanding Race in a "Post-racial" World.* 2nd ed. Lanham, MD: Rowman & Littlefield.

Case, Kim, ed. 2013. *Deconstructing Privilege: Teaching and Learning as Allies in the Classroom.* New York: Routledge.

Clandinin, D. Jean, and Heather Raymond. 2006. "Note on Narrating Disability." *Equity & Excellence in Education* 39, no. 2: 101–4.

Coates, Rodney D. 2011. "Covert Racism: An Introduction." In *Covert Racism: Theories, Institutions, and Experiences,* edited by Rodney D. Coates. Leiden, Netherlands: Brill.

Collins, Patricia Hill. 2000. *Black Feminist Thought: Knowledge, Consciousness, and the Politics of Empowerment.* 2nd ed. New York: Routledge.

——. 2004. *Black Sexual Politics: African Americans, Gender, and the New Racism.* New York: Routledge.

Connor, David J. 2006. "Michael's Story: 'I Get into Such Trouble Just by Walking': Narrative Knowing and Life at the Intersections of Learning Disability, Race, and Class." *Equity & Excellence in Education* 39, no. 2: 154–65.

Crenshaw, Kimberlé. 1991. "Mapping the Margins: Intersectionality, Identity Politics, and Violence against Women of Color." *Stanford Law Review* 43, no. 6: 1241–99.

Cunnigen, Donald, and Marino A. Bruce, eds. 2010. *Race in the Age of Obama.* Bingley, England: Emerald Books.

Dasien, Andrew. 2008. "Hutu and Tutsi before Colonialism." All Quiet on the Quaker Front: A U.S. Quaker in Burundi, June 12. Accessed August 3, 2015. http://www .quakerfront.com/2008/ 06/12/hutu-tutsi-before-colonialism.

Davis, Angela Y. 1983. *Women, Race and Class.* New York: Vintage Books.

——. 1990. *Women, Culture and Politics.* New York: Vintage Books.

Desmond, Matthew, and Mustafa Emirbayer. 2010. *Racial Domination, Racial Progress: The Sociology of Race in America.* New York: McGraw-Hill.

Espiritu, Yen Le. 1994. *Asian American Panethnicity: Bridging Institutions and Identities.* Philadelphia: Temple University Press.

Feagin, Joe R. 2000. *Racist America: Roots, Current Realities, and Future Reparations.* New York: Routledge.

——. 2010. *The White Racial Frame: Centuries of Racial Framing and Counter-framing.* New York: Routledge.

Feagin, Joe R., and José A. Cobas. 2013. *Latinos Facing Racism: Discrimination, Resistance, and Endurance.* Boulder, CO: Paradigm.

Fearon, James D. 2002. "Ethnic Structure and Cultural Diversity around the World: A Cross-National Data Set on Ethnic Groups." Paper presented at the annual meeting of the American Political Science Association, Boston, August 28.

Ferber, Abby L. 2012. "The Culture of Privilege: Color-Blindness, Postfeminism, and Christonormativity." *Journal of Social Issues* 68, no. 1: 63–77.

Ferber, Abby L., Christina M. Jiménez, Andrea O'Reilly Herrera, and Dena R. Samuels, eds. 2009. *The Matrix Reader: Examining the Dynamics of Oppression and Privilege.* Boston: McGraw Hill.

Ferber, Abby L., and Dena R. Samuels. 2010. "Oppression without Bigots." SWS Factsheet, Sociologists for Women in Society. Accessed April 4, 2017. https://www .socwomen.org/wp-content/ uploads/2010/05/fact_3-2010-oppression.pdf.

Ferrante, Joan, and Prince Brown Jr. 2001. *The Social Construction of Race and Ethnicity in the United States.* 2nd ed. Upper Saddle River, NJ: Prentice Hall.

Fields, Karen E., and Barbara J. Fields. 2012. *Racecraft: The Soul of Inequality in American Life.* London: Verso Books.

Fish, Jefferson M. 2011. "What Does the Brazilian Census Tell Us about Race?" Looking in the Cultural Mirror (blog), *Psychology Today,* December 6. Accessed April 4, 2017. https://www .psychologytoday.com/ blog/looking-in-the-cultural-mirror/201112/what-does-the-brazilian-census-tell-us-about-race.

Freedman, Estelle B. 2002. *No Turning Back: The History of Feminism and the Future of Women.* New York: Ballantine Books.

Frye, Marilyn. 2007. *The Politics of Reality: Essays in Feminist Theory.* Berkeley, CA: Crossing Press.

Gallagher, Charles. 2009. "Color-Blinded America or How the Media and Politics Have Made Racism and Racial Inequality Yesterday's Social Problem." In *The Matrix Reader: Examining the Dynamics of Oppression and Privilege,* edited by Abby L. Ferber, Christina M. Jiménez, Andrea O'Reilly Herrera, and Dena R. Samuels, 548–51. Boston: McGraw-Hill.

Gans, Herbert J. 1971. "The Uses of Poverty: The Poor Pay All." *Social Policy* 2, no. 2 (July/August): 14–21.

Garcia, Alma M. 1997. *Chicana Feminist Thought: The Basic Historical Writings.* New York: Routledge.

Gould, Stephen Jay. 1981. *The Mismeasure of Man.* New York: W. W. Norton.

Graham, David. 2016. "The Stubborn Persistence of Confederate Monuments." *Atlantic,* April. Accessed April 30, 2017. https://www .theatlantic.com/politics/ archive/2016/04/the-stubborn-persistence-of-confederate-monuments/479751.

Grosfoguel, Ramán. 2004. "Race and Ethnicity or Racialized

Ethnicities? Identities within Global Coloniality." *Ethnicities* 4: 315–36.

Haney López, Ian. 2006. *White by Law: The Legal Construction of Race.* Rev. ed. New York: New York University Press.

Hannah-Jones, Nikole. 2016. "The End of the Postracial Myth." *New York Times Magazine,* November 15. Accessed March 5, 2017. https://www.nytimes.com/interactive/2016/11/20/magazine/donald-trumps-america-iowa-race.html.

Harding, Sandra, ed. 1993. *The "Racial" Economy of Science: Toward a Democratic Future.* Bloomington: Indiana University Press.

Hartigan, John, Jr. 2010. *Race in the 21st Century: Ethnographic Approaches.* New York: Oxford University Press.

Hillinbrand, Carole. 2000. *The Crusades: Islamic Perspectives.* New York: Routledge.

hooks, bell. 2000. *Feminist Theory from Margin to Center.* 2nd ed. Cambridge, MA: South End Press.

Hull, Gloria T., Patricia Bell Scott, and Barbara Smith. 2015. *All the Women Are White, All the Blacks Are Men, but Some of Us Are Brave: Black Women's Studies.* 2nd ed. New York: Feminist Press.

Irons, Jenny. 2010. *Reconstituting Whiteness: The Mississippi State Sovereignty Commission.* Nashville: Vanderbilt University Press.

Jacobson, Matthew Frye. 1998. *Whiteness of a Different Color: European Immigrants and the Alchemy of Race.* Cambridge, MA: Harvard University Press.

Johnson, Allan G. 2006. *Privilege, Power, and Difference.* 2nd ed. Boston: McGraw-Hill.

Ken, Ivy. 2008. "Beyond the Intersection: A New Culinary Metaphor for Race-Class-Gender Studies." *Sociological Theory* 26, no. 2: 152–72.

Khan, M. A. 2009. *Islamic Jihad: A Legacy of Forced Conversion, Imperialism, and Slavery.* Bloomington, IN: iUniverse.

Landrieu, Mitch. 2017. "We Can't Walk Away from This Truth." *Atlantic,* May. Accessed April 30, 2017. https://www.theatlantic.com/politics/archive/2017/05/we-cant-walk-away-from-this-truth/527721.

Linshi, Jack. 2014. "10 Million Americans Switched Their Race or Ethnicity for the Census." *Time,* August 7. Accessed April 7, 2017. http://time.com/3087649/census-race-ethnicity-report.

Lorde, Audre. (1984) 2007. *Sister Outsider: Essays and Poems.* Berkeley, CA: Crossing Press.

Markus, Hazel Rose, and Paula M. L. Moya. 2010. *Doing Race: 21 Essays for the 21st Century.* New York: W. W. Norton.

McIntosh, Peggy. 1988. "White Privilege and Male Privilege: A Personal Account of Coming to See Correspondences through Work in Women's Studies." Working Paper 189, Wellesley College Center for Research on Women.

McNamee, Stephen, and Robert K. Miller Jr. 2014. *The Meritocracy Myth.* 3rd ed. Lanham, MD: Rowman & Littlefield.

Moore, Eddie, Jr., Marguerite W. Penick-Parks, and Ali Michael, eds. 2015. *Everyday White People Confront Racial and Social Injustice: 15 Stories.* Sterling, VA: Stylus.

Morrison, Toni. 1992. *Playing in the Dark: Whiteness and the Literary Imagination.* New York: Vintage Books.

Mills, Charles. 1997. *The Racial Contract.* Ithaca, NY: Cornell University Press.

National Education Association. 2015. "Ensuring Safe Schools for All Students." Accessed August 3, 2015. http://www.nea.org/tools/30437.htm.

Omi, Michael, and Howard Winant. 1994. *Racial Formation in the United States: From the 1960s to the 1990s.* 2nd ed. New York: Routledge.

Ortiz, Vilma, and Edward Telles. 2012. "Racial Identity and Racial Treatment of Mexican Americans." *Race and Social Problems* 4, no. 1 (April): 41–56.

Painter, Nell Irvin. 2015. "What Is Whiteness?" *New York Times Sunday Review,* June 6. Accessed August 4, 2015. http://www.nytimes.com/2015/06/21/opinion/sunday/what-is-whiteness.html?_r=0.

Park, Madison. 2017. "Removal of Confederate Monuments Stirs Backlash in Statehouses." CNN, May 12. Accessed June 10, 2017. http://www.cnn.com/2017/05/12/us/confederate-monument-state-bills/index.html.

Perez, Chris. 2015. "Meet the Biracial Twins No One Believes Are Sisters." *New York Post,* March 2. Accessed June 7, 2017. http://nypost.com/2015/03/02/meet-the-bi-racial-twins-no-one-believes-are-sisters.

Plaut, Victoria C. 2010. "Diversity Science: Why and How Difference Makes a Difference." *Psychological*

Inquiry 21, no. 2: 77–99. doi:10.1080/10478401003 676501.

Portis, Larry. 2007. "'Arabs' and 'Jews' as Significant Others: Zionism and the Ambivalence of 'Orientalism' in the United-Statesian Imagination." *Middle Ground: Journal of Literary and Cultural Encounters* 1: 75–96.

Radford, Tim. 2015. "Irish DNA Originated in Middle East and Eastern Europe." *Guardian,* December 28. Accessed April 5, 2017. https://www.theguardian .com/science/2015/dec/28/ origins-of-the-irish-down-to-mass-migration-ancient-dna-confirms.

Ritvo, Harriet. 1997. *The Platypus and the Mermaid, and Other Figments of the Classifying Imagination.* Cambridge, MA: Harvard University Press.

Robnett, Belinda. 1999. *How Long? How Long? African-American Women in the Struggle for Civil Rights.* Oxford: Oxford University Press.

Ruiz, Vicki L. 1999. *From Out of the Shadows: Mexican Women in Twentieth-Century America.* Oxford: Oxford University Press.

Rumbaut, Ruben. 2011. "Pigments of Our Imagination: The Racialization of the Hispanic-Latino Category." Immigration Policy Institute, April 27. Accessed September 13, 2016. http:// www.migrationpolicy .org/article/pigments-our-imagination-racialization-hispanic-latino-category.

Russell, Joseph, and Jeanne Batalova. 2012. "European Immigrants in the United States." Migration Policy Institute, July 26. Accessed

August 18, 2016. http://www .migrationpolicy.org/article/ european-immigrants-united-states-1.

Segal, Ronald. 2001. *Islam's Black Slaves: The Other Black Diaspora.* New York: Farrar, Straus and Giroux.

Smaje, Chris. 2000. *Natural Hierarchies: The Historical Sociology of Race and Caste.* Oxford: Blackwell.

Smedley, Audrey. 2007. *Race in North America: Origin and Evolution of a Worldview.* 3rd ed. Boulder, CO: Westview Press.

Snively, Gloria, and John Corsiglia. 2001. "Discovering Indigenous Science: Implications for Science Education." *Science Education* 85, no. 1: 6–34.

Sollors, Werner, ed. 1989. *The Invention of Ethnicity.* New York: Oxford University Press.

Spade, Joan Z., and Jeanne H. Ballantine, eds. 2011. *Schools and Society: A Sociological Approach to Education.* Thousand Oaks, CA: Sage.

Spelman, Elizabeth V. 1988. *Inessential Woman: Problems of Exclusion in Feminist Thought.* Boston: Beacon Press.

Sue, Derald Wing. 2010. *Microaggressions in Everyday Life: Race, Gender, and Sexual Orientation.* Hoboken, NJ: John Wiley.

Takei, Isao, and Arthur Sakamoto. 2011. "Poverty among Asian Americans in the 21st Century." *Sociological Perspectives* 54, no. 2: 251–76.

Telles, Edward, and the Project on Ethnicity and Race in Latin America. 2014. *Pigmentocracies: Ethnicity, Race, and Color in Latin America.* Chapel Hill:

University of North Carolina Press.

Tochluk, Shelly. 2008. *Witnessing Whiteness: First Steps toward an Antiracist Practice and Culture.* Lanham, MD: Rowman & Littlefield.

U.S. Bureau of Labor Statistics. 2010. *Highlights of Women's Earnings in 2009.* Report 1025, June. Washington, DC: U.S. Department of Labor. Accessed April 1, 2017. https://www .bls.gov/opub/reports/ womens-earnings/archive/ womensearnings_2009.pdf

U.S. Census Bureau. 2012. "2010 Census Shows Nearly Half of American Indians and Alaska Natives Report Multiple Races." Press release, January 25. Accessed April 1, 2017. https://www.census .gov/newsroom/releases/ archives/2010_census/cb12-cn06.html.

———. 2015. "Annual Estimates of the Resident Population by Sex, Race Alone or in Combination, and Hispanic Origin for the United States, States, and Counties: April 1, 2010 to July 1, 2014." American FactFinder. Accessed June 12, 2017. https://factfinder.census .gov/faces/tableservices/ jsf/pages/productview .xhtml?src=bkmk.

Van Ausdale, Debra, and Joe R. Feagin. 2001. *The First R: How Children Learn Race and Racism.* Lanham, MD: Rowman & Littlefield.

Villalon, Roberta. 2010. *Violence against Latina Immigrants: Citizenship, Inequality, and Community.* New York: New York University Press.

Wade, Lizzie. 2014. "Genetic Study Reveals Surprising Ancestry of Many Americans." *Science,*

December 18. Accessed April 2, 2017. http://www.sciencemag.org/news/2014/12/genetic-study-reveals-surprising-ancestry-many-americans.

Walters, Alicia. 2015. "I Became a Black Woman in Spokane. But, Rachel Dolezal, I Was a Black Girl First." *Guardian,* June 14. Accessed August 3, 2015. http://www.theguardian.com/commentisfree/2015/jun/14/became-a-black-woman-spokane-rachel-dolezal-black-girl.

Ware, Kallistos. 1980. *The Orthodox Church.* New York: Penguin.

Warren, Carroll. 1993. *The Glory of Christendom.* Front Royal, VA: Christendom Press.

Wootson, Cleve R., Jr. 2017. "New Orleans Protesters Launch Last-Ditch Effort to Protect Confederate Monuments." *Chicago Tribune,* April 30. Accessed April 30, 2017. http://www.chicagotribune.com/news/nationworld/ct-new-orleans-confederate-monuments-20170430-story.html.

Wright, Louis B. 1970. *Gold, Glory and the Gospel.* New York: Atheneum Press.

Yoshino, Kenji. 2007. *Covering: The Hidden Assault on Our Civil Liberties.* New York: Random House.

Yudell, Michael, Dorothy Roberts, Rob DeSalle, Rob, and Sarah Tishkoff. 2016. "Taking Race Out of Human Genetics." *Science* 351, no. 6273: 564–65.

Zong, Jie, and Jeanne Batalova. 2016. "Asian Immigrants in the United States." Migration Policy Institute, January 6. Accessed April 4, 2017. http://www.migrationpolicy.org/article/asian-immigrants-united-states.

Zuberi, Tukufu. 2001. *Thicker than Blood: How Racial Statistics Lie.* Minneapolis: University of Minnesota Press.

■ CHAPTER 2

Adelman, Jeremy, and Stephen Aron. 1999. "From Borderlands to Borders: Empires, Nation-States, and the Peoples in between in North American History." *American Historical Review* 104, no. 3 (June): 814–41.

Alegria, Ricardo. 1990. *Juan Garrido, el Conquistador Negro en Antillas, Florida, Mexico y California c. 1503–1540.* San Juan, Puerto Rico: Centro de Estudios Avanzados de Puerto y el Caribe.

Allen, Theodore W. 1997. *The Invention of the White Race: The Origin of Racial Oppression in Anglo-America.* New York: Verso Books.

———. 2012. *The Invention of the White Race: The Origin of Racial Oppression in Anglo-America.* Vol. 2. New York: Verso Books.

Aptheker, Herbert. 1993. *African Negro Slave Revolts.* 6th ed. New York: International Publishers.

Arends, Jacques. 1995. "Demographic Factors in the Formation of Sranan." In *The Early Stages of Creolization,* edited by Jacques Arends, 233–86. Amsterdam: John Benjamins.

Arnaiz-Villena, C. Parga-Lorazano, E. Moreno, C. Areces, D. Rey, and P. Gomez-Prieto. 2010. "The Origin of Amerindians and the Peopling of the Americas According to HLA Genes: Admixture with Asian and Pacific People." *Current Genomics* 11, no. 2 (April): 103–14.

Asbury, Herbert. (1936) 2003. *The French Quarter: An Informal History of the New Orleans Underworld.* New York: Alfred A. Knopf.

Barrera, Mario. 1976. "Colonial Labor and Theories of Inequality: The Case of International Harvester." *Review of Radical Political Economics* 8, no. 2: 1–18.

Beal, Timothy K. 2008. *Religion in America: A Short History.* London: Oxford University Press.

Beckles, Hilary McD. 1990. "A 'Riotous and Unruly Lot': Irish Indentured Servants and Freemen in the English West Indies, 1644–1713." *William and Mary Quarterly* 47, no. 4 (October): 503–22.

Belchior, Elias. 2007. "White Rights, Black Rights, Human Rights." In *Human Rights in Brazil 2007,* edited by Evanize Sydow e Maria Luisa Mendonça. São Paulo: Social Network for Justice and Human Rights.

Belmessous, Saliha. 2005. "Assimilation and Racialism in Seventeenth and Eighteenth-Century French Colonial Policy." *American Historical Review* 110, no. 2 (April): 322–49.

Beltran, Erika. 2010. Review of *New England Frontier: Puritans and Indians 1620–1675,* by Alden T. Vaughan. Race, Class and Ethnicity in American History (blog), October 17. Accessed May 30, 2017. http://todiefree .blogspot.com/2010/10/new-england-frontier-puritans-and .html.

Berlin, Ira. 1998. *Many Thousands Gone: The First Two Centuries of Slavery in North America.* Boston: Harvard University Press.

———. 2003. *Generations of Captivity: A History of African-American Slaves.* Cambridge, MA: Harvard University Press.

Bernhard, Virginia. 1999. *Slaves and Slaveholders in Bermuda, 1616–1782.* Columbia: University of Missouri Press.

Biancardi, Paul. 2015. "ESPN 100: Where Would We Have Ranked Thon Maker?" ESPN, August 26. Accessed June 13, 2017. http:// www.espn.com/blog/ ncbrecruiting/on-the-trail/ insider/post?id=14409.

Blackman, Robin. 1997. *The Making of New World Slavery: From the Baroque to the Modern, 1492–1800.* New York: Verso Books.

Blauner, Robert. 1972. *Racial Oppression in America.* New York: Harper and Brothers.

Bonilla-Silva, Eduardo. 2008. "'Look, a Negro': Reflections on the Human Rights Approach to Racial Inequality." In *Globalization and America: Race, Human Rights, and Inequality,* edited by Angela J. Hattery, David G. Embrick, and Earl Smith, 9–22. Lanham, MD: Rowman & Littlefield.

Bowles, Samuel, and Herbert Gintis. 2011. *Schooling in Capitalist America: Educational Reform and the Contradictions of Economic Life.* New York: Haymarket Books.

Boxer, C. R. 1975. *Women in Iberian Expansion Overseas, 1415–1815.* New York: Oxford University Press.

Bradford, William. 1901. *Of Plymouth Plantation.* Boston: Wright and Potter.

Breen, T. H. 1973. "A Changing Labor Force and Race Relations in Virginia 1660–1710." *Journal of Social History* 7, no. 1 (Autumn): 3–25.

Brown, Kathleen. 1996. *Good Wives, Nasty Wenches, and Anxious Patriarchs: Gender, Race, and Power in Colonial Virginia.* Chapel Hill: University of North Carolina Press.

Buchanan, Kelly. 2011. "Slavery in the French Colonies: Le Code Noir (the Black Code) of 1685." In Custodia Legis (blog), Law Library of Congress, January 13. Accessed May 5, 2016. https://blogs.loc.gov/ law/2011/01/slavery-in-the-french-colonies.

Caspari, Rachel 2003. "From Types to Populations: A Century of Race, Physical Anthropology, and the Anthropological Association." *American Anthropology* 105, no. 1: 65–76.

Chambliss, William J. 1989. "State-Organized Crime— The American Society of Criminology, 1988 Presidential Address." *Criminology* 27, no. 2: 183–208.

Childress, Sarah. 2014. "School Segregation Is Back, 60 Years after 'Brown.'" *Frontline,* PBS, May 15. Accessed April 9, 2017. http://www.pbs.org/wgbh/ frontline/article/report-school-segregation-is-back-60-years-after-brown.

Clayton, Lawrence. 2009. "Bartolomé de las Casas and the African Slave Trade." *History Compass* 7, no. 6 (November): 1526–41.

Clough, Patricia Ticineto. 2003. "Affect and Control: Rethinking the Body 'beyond Sex and Gender.'" *Feminist Theory* 4, no. 3: 359–64.

Cohn, D'Vera, and Andrea Caumont. 2016. "10 Demographic Trends That Are Shaping the U.S. and the World." Fact Tank, Pew Research Center, March 31. Accessed June 20, 2017. http://www.pewresearch.org/ fact-tank/2016/03/31/10-demographic-trends-that-are-shaping-the-u-s-and-the-world.

Colburn, David R., and Jane L. Landers, eds. 1995. *The African American Heritage of Florida.* Gainesville: University Press of Florida.

Conley, Dalton. 2011. *You May Ask Yourself. A Guide to Thinking Like a Sociologist.* 2nd ed. New York: W. W. Norton.

Cook, Sherburne F. 1976. *The Population of the California Indians, 1769–1970.* Berkeley: University of California Press.

Corris, Peter. 1973. *Passage, Port and Plantation: A History of Solomon Islands Migration, 1870–1940.* Melbourne: Melbourne University Press.

Deagan, Kathleen. 1983. "Spanish-Indian Interaction in Sixteenth-Century Florida and Hispaniola." In *Cultures in Contact,* edited by William Fitzhugh, 281–318. Washington, DC: Smithsonian Institution Press.

———. 1985. *Spanish St. Augustine: The Archaeology of a Colonial Creole Community.* New York: Academic Press.

———. 1996. "Colonial Transformations: Euro-American Cultural Genesis in the Early Spanish American Colonies." *Journal of Anthropological Research* 52, no. 2 (Summer): 135–60.

———. 2004. "Reconsidering Taíno Social Dynamics after Spanish Conquest: Gender and Class in Culture Contact Studies." *American Antiquity* 69: 597–626.

Deagan, Kathleen, and José María Cruxent. 1993. "From Contact to *Criollos*: The Archaeology of Spanish Colonization in Hispaniola." *Proceedings of the British Academy* 81: 67–104.

———. 2002. *Columbus's Outpost among the Taínos: Spain and America at La Isabela, 1493–1498*. New Haven, CT: Yale University Press.

Deloria, Vine, Jr. 1988. *Custer Died for Your Sins: An Indian Manifesto*. Oklahoma City: University of Oklahoma Press.

Diamond, Jared. 1999. *Guns, Germs, and Steel: The Fates of Human Societies*. New York: W. W. Norton.

Diggs, Irene. 1953. "Color in Colonial Spanish America." *Journal of Negro History* 38, no. 4 (October): 403–27.

Fanon, Frantz. 1965. *The Wretched of the Earth*. New York: Grove Press.

Foner, Eric. 2006. *Give Me Liberty! An American History*. Vol. 1. New York: W. W. Norton.

Frank, Andre Gunder. 1976. *On Capitalist Underdevelopment*. New York: Oxford University Press.

Frazier, E. Franklin. 1949. *The Negro in the United States*. New York: Macmillan.

Fry, Richard. 2011. "Hispanic College Enrollment Spikes, Narrowing Gaps with Other Groups." Pew Research Center, August 25. Accessed June 13, 2017. http://www.pewhispanic.org/2011/08/25/hispanic-college-enrollment-spikes-narrowing-gaps-with-other-groups.

Galenson, David W. 1984. "The Rise and Fall of Indentured Servitude in the Americas: An Economic Analysis." *Journal of Economic History* 44, no. 1 (March): 1–26.

Gallay, Alan. 2002. *The Indian Slave Trade: The Rise of the English Empire in the American South, 1670–1717*. New Haven, CT: Yale University Press.

Gardner, Charles F. 2017. "Bucks Rookie Thon Maker Could Be All-Star in the Making." *Milwaukee Journal Sentinel,* February 19. Accessed April 5, 2017. http://www.jsonline.com/story/sports/nba/bucks/2017/02/19/bucks-rookie-thon-maker-could-all-star-making/98043082.

Garrigus, John D. 2007. "Opportunist or Patriot? Julien Raimond (1744–1801) and the Haitian Revolution." *Slavery and Abolition* 28, no. 1 (April): 1–21.

Gill, Harold B. 2003. "Colonial Germ Warfare." *Colonial Williamsburg Journal* 4 (Spring). Accessed May 30, 2017. http://www.history.org/foundation/journal/spring04/warfare.cfm.

Gould, Stephen Jay. 1981. *The Mismeasure of Man*. New York: W. W. Norton.

Goyette, Braden, and Alissa Scheller. 2016. "15 Charts That Prove That We're Far from Post-racial." Huffington Post, March 3. Accessed June 13, 2017. http://www.huffingtonpost.com/2014/07/02/civil-rights-act-anniversary-racism-charts_n_5521104.html.

Greene, Lorenzo Johnston. 1942. *The Negro in Colonial New England, 1620–1776*. New York: Columbia University Press.

Greer, Allan. 1997. *The People of New France*. Toronto: University of Toronto Press.

Gutiérrez, Gustavo. 1974. *A Theology of Liberation*. Maryknoll, NY: Orbis Books.

Gutiérrez, José Angel, Michelle Meléndez, and Sonia Adriana Noyola. 2007. *Chicanas in Charge: Texas Women in the Public Arena*. Lanham, MD: AltaMira Press.

Haan, Richard L. 1973. "Another Example of Stereotypes on the Early American Frontier: The Imperialistic Historians and the American Indian." *Ethnohistory* 20, no. 2 (Spring): 143–52.

Hall, Gwendolyn Midlo. 1992. *Africans in Colonial Louisiana*. Baton Rouge: Louisiana State University Press.

Harper, Douglas. 2003. "Colonial Slavery: Northern Profits from Slavery." Varsity Tutors, Archiving Early America. Accessed May 30, 2017. http://www.earlyamerica.com/review/2004_summer_fall/northern_profits.htm.

Hening, William Waller. 1819. *The Statutes at Large, Being the Collection of All the Laws of Virginia from the Third Session of the Legislature in the Year 1619*. 13 vols. Richmond, VA: W. Gray Printers.

Holmes, Jack D. L. 1970. "The Abortive Slave Revolt at Pointe Coupee, Louisiana, 1795." *Louisiana History* 11, no. 4: 341–62.

Hugh, Thomas. 1997. *The Slave Trade*. New York: Simon & Schuster.

Jackson, Robert. 2006. "República de Indios." In *Iberia and the Americas: Culture, Politics, and History—A Multidisciplinary Encyclopedia,* edited by J. Michael Francis, 901–3. Santa Barbara, CA: ABC-CLIO.

Janiewski, Dolores. 1995. "Gendering, Racializing and Classifying: Settler Colonization in the United States, 1950–1990." In *Unsettling Settler Societies: Articulations of Gender, Race, Ethnicity and Class,* edited by Daiva K. Stasiulis and Nira Yuval-Davis. London: Sage.

Jennings, Francis. 1975. *The Invasion of America: Indians, Colonialism, and the Cant of Conquest.* New York: W. W. Norton.

Karenga, Maulana. 2002. *Introduction to Black Studies.* 3rd ed. Los Angeles: University of Sankore Press.

Keen, Benjamin, and Keith Haynes. 2009. *A History of Latin America.* Boston: Houghton Mifflin Harcourt.

Kit-Powell, Rodney. 2013. "Seminole Wars Shaped Florida's History." *Tampa Tribune,* July 14. Accessed September 9, 2013, http://tbo.com/events/seminole-wars-shaped-floridas-history-20130714.

Kotkin, Joel. 2010. "The Changing Demographics of America." *Smithsonian Magazine,* August. Accessed September 9, 2013. http://www.smithsonianmag.com/travel/the-changing-demographics-of-america-538284.

Kramsch, Olivier Thomas, and Sabine Motzenbacker. 2004. "On the 'Pirate Frontier': Re-conceptualizing the Space of Ocean Governance in Light of the *Prestige* Disaster." Research Team Governance and Place Working Paper Series 2004/1, University of Nijmegen. Accessed September 9, 2013. http://www.ru.nl/publish/pages/515103/2004-1.pdf.

Krogstad, Jens Manuel. 2015. "Reflecting a Racial Shift, 78 Counties Turned Majority-Minority since 2000." Fact Tank, Pew Research Center, April 8. Accessed May 8, 2017. http://www.pewresearch.org/fact-tank/2015/04/08/reflecting-a-racial-shift-78-counties-turned-majority-minority-since-2000.

Kromm, Chris, and Sue Sturgis. 2008. *Hurricane Katrina and the Guiding Principles on Internal Displacement: A Global Human Rights Perspective on a National Disaster.* Durham, NC: Institute for Southern Studies. Accessed June 13, 2017. https://www.brookings.edu/wp-content/uploads/2012/04/0114_ISSKatrina.pdf.

Landers, Jane L. 1984. "Spanish Sanctuary: Fugitives in Florida, 1687–1790." *Florida Historical Quarterly* 62 (January): 296–313.

———. 1997. "Africans in Spanish Colonies." *Historical Archaeology* 31, no. 1: 84–103.

Lange, Matthew, James Mahoney, and Mathias vom Hau. 2006. "Colonialism and Development: A Comparative Analysis of Spanish and British Colonies." *American Journal of Sociology* 111, no. 5 (March): 1412–62.

Lewis, Kevin, Marco Gonzalez, and Jason Kaufman. 2011. "Social Selection and Peer Influence in an Online Social Network." *Proceedings of the National Academy of Sciences* 109, no. 1: 68–72.

Li, Stephanie. 2007. "Resistance, Silence, and Placées: Charles Bon's Octoroon Mistress and Louisa Picquet." *American Literature* 79, no. 1 (March): 85–112.

Linnaeus, Carolus. 1758. *Systemae Naturae.* 10th ed. Stockholm: Laurentii Salvii.

Lord, Lewis, and Sarah Burke. 1991. "America Before Columbus." *U.S. News & World Report,* July 8, 22–27. Accessed June 1, 2017. http://web.archive.org/web/20020827104452/http://www.millersville.edu/~columbus/data/art/LORD-01.ART.

Maciag, Mike. 2015. "A State-by-State Look at Growing Minority Populations." *Governing,* June 25. Accessed April 4, 2017. http://www.governing.com/topics/urban/gov-majority-minority-populations-in-states.html.

Mann, Charles. 2005. *1491: New Revelations of the Americas before Columbus.* New York: Borzoi Books

Martinez, Maria Elena. 2004. "Limpieza de Sangre, Racial Violence, and Gendered Power in Early Colonial Mexico." *William and Mary Quarterly,* 3rd ser., 61, no. 3 (July): 479–520.

———. 2008. *Limpieza de Sangre, Religion, and Gender in Colonial Mexico.* Stanford, CA: Stanford University Press.

Martinez-Alier, Veren. (1974) 1989. *Marriage, Class and Color in Nineteenth-Century Cuba:*

A Study of Racial Attitudes and Sexual Values in a Slave Society. Ann Arbor: Michigan University Press.

McEwan, Bonnie G. 1991. "The Archaeology of Women in the Spanish New World." Historical Archaeology 25, no. 4: 33–41.

Mendoza, Ruben. 1997. "Metallurgy in Meso and Native America." In Encyclopaedia of the History of Science, Technology, and Medicine in Non-Western Cultures, edited by H. Selin, 702–6. Dordrecht: Kluwer Academic.

Mills, Charles. 1997. The Racial Contract. Ithaca, NY: Cornell University Press.

Moitt, Bernard. 2001. Women and Slavery in the French Antilles, 1635–1848. Bloomington: Indiana University Press.

Moje, Elizabeth Birr, Josephine Peyton Young, John E. Readence, and David W. Moore. 2000. "Reinventing Adolescent Literacy for New Times: Perennial and Millennial Issues." Journal of Adolescent & Adult Literacy 43, no. 5: 400–410.

National Archives. 2000. "Educator Resources: The Amistad Case." Accessed April 23, 2013. http://www .archives.gov/education/ lessons/amistad.

Novack, George E. 1939. "Negro Slavery in North America." New International 5, no. 10 (October): 305–8. Accessed April 23, 2013. https:// www.marxists.org/archive/ novack/1939/10/x01.htm.

Orfield, Gary. 2009. Reviving the Goal of an Integrated Society: A 21st Century Challenge. Los Angeles: UCLA Civil Rights Project.

Palmer, Vernon V. 1995. "The Origins and Authors of the Code Noir." Louisiana Law Review 56, no. 363: 363–408.

Parise, Agustin. 2008. "Slave Laws and Labor Activities During the Spanish Colonial Period: A Study of the South American Region of Río de la Plata." Rutgers Law Record 32, no. 1: 1–39.

Parker, Martin. 2009. "Pirates, Merchants and Anarchists: Representations of International Business." Management and Organizational History 4, no. 2: 167–85.

Pateman, Carole. 1988. The Sexual Contract. Stanford, CA: Stanford University Press.

PBS. 2000. "Africans in America: America's Journey through Slavery." Accessed April 22, 2013. http://www.pbs.org/ wgbh/aia/part1/1p285.html.

Perrin, Andrew. 2015. "Social Media Usage: 2005–2015." Pew Research Center, October 8. Accessed June 13, 2017. http://www. pewinternet.org/2015/10/08/ social-networking- usage-2005-2015.

Phillips, William D. 1985. Slavery from Roman Times to the Early Transatlantic Trade. Minneapolis: University of Minnesota Press.

Pitts, Leonard. 2012. "A Whiter Shade of Privilege." Columbia Daily Tribune, March 28. Accessed April 22, 2013. http://m .columbiatribune.com/ news/2012/mar/28/a- whiter-shade-of- privilege/?commentary.

Postma, Johannes. 1990. The Dutch in the Atlantic Slave Trade, 1600–1815. Cambridge: Cambridge University Press.

Rasmussen, Daniel. 2011. "American Rising": When Slaves Attacked New Orleans. New York: HarperCollins.

Rediker, Marcus Buford. 2004. Villains of All Nations: Atlantic Pirates in the Golden Age. London: Bath Press.

Reynolds, David S. 2005. John Brown, Abolitionist: The Man Who Killed Slavery, Sparked the Civil War, and Seeded Civil Rights. New York: Vintage Press.

Riding, Alan. 1992. "6 Ships, 2 Queens, Many Headaches." New York Times, March 15. Accessed June 1, 2017. http://www .nytimes.com/1992/03/15/ movies/film-6-ships-2- queens-many-headaches. html?ref=alanriding.

Robenstine, Clark. 1992. "French Colonial Policy and the Education of Women and Minorities: Louisiana in the Early Eighteenth Century." History of Education Quarterly 32, no. 2 (Summer): 193–211.

Roediger, David R. 2007. The Wages of Whiteness: Race and the Making of the American Working Class. Chicago: Haymarket Press.

Rupp, Leila J. 2001. "Toward a Global History of Same-Sex Sexuality." Journal of the History of Sexuality 10, no. 2 (April): 287–302.

Rushforth, Brett. 2003. "'A Little Flesh We Offer You': The Origins of Indian Slavery in New France." William and Mary Quarterly, 3rd ser., 60, no. 4 (October): 777–808.

Sassaman, Kenneth E. 2005. "Poverty Point as Structure, Event, Process." Journal of Archaeological Method and Theory 12, no. 4 (December): 335–64.

Schafer, Daniel L. 1993. "'A Class of People Neither Freemen nor Slave': From Spanish Race Relations in Florida, 1821–1861." *Journal of Social History* 26, no. 3 (Spring): 587–609.

Shin, Hyon B., and Robert A. Kominski. 2010. *Language Use in the United States: 2007.* Washington, DC: U.S. Census Bureau.

Shippen, Peggy. 2004. "Sex Ratios." In *Women in Early America: Struggle, Survival, and Freedom,* edited by Dorothy A. Mays, 356–58. Santa Barbara, CA: ABC-CLIO.

Simms, Ellen Yvonne. 2009. "Miscegenation and Racism: Afro-Mexicans in Colonial New Spain." *Journal of Pan African Studies* 2, no. 3 (March): 228–54.

Singler, John Victor. 1995. "The Demographics of Creole Genesis in the Caribbean: A Comparison of Martinique and Haiti." In *The Early Stages of Creolization,* edited by Jacques Arends, 203–32. Amsterdam: John Benjamins.

Smedley, Audrey. 2007. *Race in North America: Origin and Evolution of a Worldview.* 3rd ed. Boulder, CO: Westview Press.

Smith, Charles E. 1966. "Negro-White Intermarriage: Forbidden Sexual Union." *Journal of Sex Research* 2, no. 3 (November): 169–77.

Soyinka, Wole. 1990. *Myth, Literature and the African World.* New York: Cambridge University Press.

Spade, Joan Z., and Jeanne H. Ballantine, eds. 2011. *Schools and Society: A Sociological Approach to Education.* Thousand Oaks, CA: Sage.

Spear, Jennifer M. 2003. "Colonial Intimacies: Legislating Sex in French Louisiana." *William and Mary Quarterly,* 3rd ser., 60, no. 1 (January): 75–98.

Stanish, Charles. 2000. "Negotiating Rank in an Imperial State: Lake Titicaca Basin Elite under Inca and Spanish Control." In *Hierarchies in Action: Cui Bono?,* edited by Michael W. Diel. Carbondale: Southern Illinois University.

Stasiulis, Daiva K., and Radha Jhappan. 1995. "The Fractious Politics of a Settler Society: Canada." In *Unsettling Settler Societies: Articulations of Gender, Race, Ethnicity and Class,* edited by Daiva K. Stasiulis and Nira Yuval-Davis. London: Sage.

Stasiulis, Daiva K., and Nira Yuval-Davis. 1995. "Beyond Dichotomies: Gender, Race, Ethnicity and Class in Settler Societies." In *Unsettling Settler Societies: Articulations of Gender, Race, Ethnicity and Class,* edited by Daiva K. Stasiulis and Nira Yuval-Davis. London: Sage.

Stern, Steve J. 1982. *Peru's Indian Peoples and the Challenge of Spanish Conquest: Huamanga to 1640.* Madison: University of Wisconsin Press.

Stinchcombe, Arthur L. 1994. "Freedom and Oppression of Slaves in the Eighteenth-Century Caribbean." *American Sociological Review* 59, no. 6 (December): 911–29.

Stolcke, Verena. 2004. "New World Engendered: The Making of the Iberian Transatlantic Empires." In *A Companion to Gender History,* edited by Teresa

A. Meade and Merry E. Wiesner-Hanks. Oxford: Blackwell.

Stoler, Ann L. 1989. "Making Empire Respectable: The Politics of Race and Sexual Morality in 20th-Century Colonial Cultures." *American Ethnologists* 16, no. 4 (November): 634–60.

Strommen, Linda Teran, and Barbara Fowles Mates. 2004. "Learning to Love Reading: Interviews with Older Children and Teens." *Journal of Adolescent & Adult Literacy* 48, no. 3: 188–2000.

Taylor, Paul, and Scott Keeter, eds. 2010. *Millennials: A Portrait of Generation Next.* Washington, DC: Pew Research Center. Accessed June 13, 2017. http://www.pewsocialtrends.org/files/2010/10/millennials-confident-connected-open-to-change.pdf.

Telles, Edward, and the Project on Ethnicity and Race in Latin America. 2014. *Pigmentocracies: Ethnicity, Race, and Color in Latin America.* Chapel Hill: University of North Carolina Press.

Thomas, G. E. 1975. "Puritans, Indians, and the Concept of Race." *New England Quarterly* 48, no. 1 (March): 3–27.

Towle, Evan B., and Lynn Marie Morgan. 2002. "Romancing the Transgender Native: Rethinking the Use of the 'Third Gender' Concept." *GLQ: A Journal of Lesbian and Gay Studies* 8, no. 4: 469–97.

Trocolli, R. 1992. "Colonization and Women's Production: The Timucua of Florida." In *Exploring Gender through Archaeology: Selected*

Papers from the 1991 Boone Conference, edited by C. Claassen and M. C. Beaudry, 95–102. Madison, WI: Prehistory Press.

Turner, Frederick J. 1920. The Frontier in American History. New York: Holt.

Tyson, Alec, and Shiva Maniam. 2016. "Behind Trump's Victory: Divisions by Race, Gender, Education." Fact Tank, Pew Research Center, November 9. Accessed June 17, 2017. http://www.pewresearch.org/fact-tank/2016/11/09/behind-trumps-victory-divisions-by-race-gender-education.

Usner, Daniel H. Jr. 1979. "From African Captivity to African Slavery: The Introduction of Black Laborers to Colonial Louisiana." Louisiana History 20, no. 1: 25–48.

Voss, Barbara. 2008. "Gender, Race, and Labor in the Archaeology of the Spanish Colonial Americas." Current Anthropology 49, no. 5 (October): 861–93.

Weatherford, Jack. 1989. "Examining the Reputation

of Christopher Columbus." Baltimore Evening Sun, October 6. Reprinted by Clergy and Laity Concerned. Accessed June 1, 2017. http://www.hartford-hwp.com/Taino/docs/columbus.html.

Weber, David J. 2000. "The Spanish Borderlands of North America: A Historiography." OAH Magazine of History 14, no. 4 (Summer): 5–11.

Williams, Joseph P. 2014. "College of Tomorrow: The Changing Demographics of the Student Body." U.S. News & World Report, September 22. Accessed April 4, 2017. https://www.usnews.com/news/college-of-tomorrow/articles/2014/09/22/college-of-tomorrow-the-changing-demographics-of-the-student-body.

Wilson, Natalie. 2011. Seduced by "Twilight": The Allure and Contradictory Messages of the Popular Saga. Jefferson, NC: McFarland.

Wolfe, Patrick. 2006. "Settler Colonialism and the

Elimination of the Native." Journal of Genocide Research 8, no. 4 (December): 387–409.

Young, R. J. C. 2001. Postcolonialism: An Historical Introduction. London: Blackwell.

Zarya, Valentina. 2016. "The Percentage of Female CEOS in the Fortune 500 Drops to 4%." Fortune, June 6. Accessed April 9, 2017. http://fortune.com/2016/06/06/women-ceos-fortune-500-2016.

Zerubavel, Eviatar. 1993. Time Maps: Collective Memory and the Social Shape of the Past. Chicago: University of Chicago Press.

Zinn, Howard. 1980. A People's History of the United States. New York: Harper & Row.

Zion, James W., and Robert Yazzie. 1997. "Indigenous Law in North America in the Wake of Conquest." Boston College International and Comparative Law Review 20: 55–84.

CHAPTER 5

Agency for Healthcare Research and Quality. 2016. 2015 National Healthcare Quality and Disparities Report and 5th Anniversary Update on the National Quality Strategy. AHRQ Pub. No. 16-0015. Washington, DC: AHRQ, U.S. Department of Health and Human Services. Accessed June 3, 2017. https://www.ahrq.gov/sites/default/files/wysiwyg/research/findings/nhqrdr/nhqdr15/2015nhqdr.pdf.

Agency for Toxic Substances and Disease Registry. 2000.

Lead Toxicity. Publication No. ATSDR-HE-CS-2001-0001. Washington, DC: U.S. Department of Health and Human Services.

Aiello, Allison E., Elaine L. Larson, and Richard Sedlak. 2008a. "Foreword." American Journal of Infection Control 36, no. 10 (suppl.): S109.

———. 2008b. "Hidden Heroes of the Health Revolution: Sanitation and Personal Hygiene." American Journal of Infection Control 36, no.10 (suppl.): S128–51.

Alsan, Marcella, and Marianne Wanamaker. "Tuskegee and the Health of Black Men." Working Paper 22323, National Bureau of Economic Research. Accessed June 27, 2017. http://www.nber.org/papers/w22323.pdf.

Amadeo, Kimberly. 2017. "Donald Trump on Health Care." The Balance, June 26. Accessed June 27, 2017. https://www.thebalance.com/how-could-trump-change-health-care-in-america-4111422.

Association of American Medical Colleges. 2012. "New Medical College Admission Test Approved: Changes Add Emphasis on Behavioral and Social Sciences." Press release, February 16. Accessed March 31, 2015. https://www.aamc.org/newsroom/newsreleases/273712/120216.html.

———. 2014. "Diversity in the Physician Workforce: Facts and Figures 2014." Accessed March 31, 2015. http://aamcdiversityfactsandfigures.org.

Barnes, Colin. 2010. "A Brief History of Discrimination and Disabled People." In *The Disability Studies Reader,* 3rd ed., edited by Lennard J. Davis, 20–32. New York: Routledge.

Blake, Kelly. 2014. "Racism May Accelerate Aging in African American Men." UMD Right Now, January 7. Accessed June 2, 2017. http://www.umdrightnow.umd.edu/news/racism-may-accelerate-aging-african-american-men.

Blumenfeld, Warren J. 2012. "One Year Sick and Then Not: On the Social Construction of Homosexuality as Disease.'" Warren Blumenfeld's Blog, December 27. Accessed December 12, 2013. http://www.warrenblumenfeld.com/?s=homosexuality+disease.

Boulware, L. Ebony, Lisa A. Cooper, Lloyd E. Ratner, Thomas A. LaVeist, and Neil R. Powe. 2003. "Race and Trust in the Health Care System." *Public Health Reports* 118, no. 4: 358–65.

Braveman, Paula. 2012. "Health Inequalities by Class and Race in the US: What Can We Learn from the Patterns?" *Social Science & Medicine* 74: 665–67.

Braveman, Paula, and Laura Gottlieb. 2014. "The Social Determinants of Health: It's Time to Consider the Causes of the Causes." *Public Health Reports* 129, no. 1 (suppl. 2): 19–31.

Brenick, Alaina, Kelly Romano, Christopher Kegler, and Lisa A. Eaton. 2017. "Understanding the Influence of Stigma and Medical Mistrust on Engagement in Routine Healthcare among Black Women Who Have Sex with Women." *LGBT Health* 4, no. 1: 4–10.

Brown, Roscoe C. 1937. "The National Negro Health Week Movement." *Journal of Negro Education* 6, no. 3 (July): 553–64.

Burrage, Rachel L., Joseph P. Gone, and Sandra L. Momper. 2016. "Urban American Indian Community Perspectives on Resources and Challenges for Youth Suicide Prevention." *American Journal of Community Psychology* 58, nos. 1–2: 136–49.

Capistrano, Christian G., Hannah Bianco, and Pilyoung Kim. 2016. "Poverty and Internalizing Symptoms: The Indirect Effect of Middle Childhood Poverty on Internalizing Symptoms via an Emotional Response Inhibition Pathway." *Frontiers in Psychology* 7. doi:10.3389/fpsyg.2016.01242.

Castillo, Michelle. 2013. "U.S. Life Expectancy Lowest among Wealthy Nations Due to Disease, Violence." CBS News, January 10. Accessed April 2, 2015. http://www.cbsnews.com/news/report-us-life-expectancy-lowest-among-wealthy-nations-due-to-disease-violence.

Centers for Disease Control and Prevention. 2017. "Stroke Facts." Accessed June 19, 2017. https://www.cdc.gov/stroke/facts.htm.

Charatz-Litt, C. 1992. "A Chronicle of Racism: The Effects of the White Medical Community on Black Health." *Journal of the National Medical Association* 84, no. 8 (August): 717–25.

Chow, Edward A., Henry Foster, Victor Gonzalez, and LaShawn McIver. 2012. "The Disparate Impact of Diabetes on Racial/Ethnic Minority Populations." *Clinical Diabetes* 30, no. 3: 130–33.

Coco, Adrienne Phelps. 2010. "Diseased, Maimed, Mutilated: Categorizations of Disability and an Ugly Law in Late Nineteenth-Century Chicago." *Journal of Social History* 44, no. 1: 23–37.

Cohen, Elizabeth, and John Bonifield. 2012. "California's Dark Legacy of Forced Sterilizations." CNN, March 15. Accessed December 11, 2012. http://www.cnn.com/2012/03/15/health/california-forced-sterilizations.

Conrad, Peter, and Valerie Leiter, eds. 2012. *The Sociology of Health and Illness: Critical Perspectives.* 9th ed. New York: Worth.

Cornwell, John. 2003. *Hitler's Scientists: Science, War, and the Devil's Pact.* New York: Penguin.

Daniels, Jessie, and Amy J. Schulz. 2006. "Constructing Whiteness in Health Disparities Research." In *Gender, Race, Class, and Health: Intersectional Approaches,* edited by Amy J. Schulz and Leith Mullings, 89–127. San Francisco: Jossey-Bass.

Davis, Lennard J. 2010. "Constructing Normalcy." In *The Disability Studies Reader,* 3rd ed., edited by Lennard J. Davis, 3–19. New York: Routledge.

Debbink, Michelle Precourt, and Michael D. M. Bader. 2011. "Racial Residential Segregation and Low Birth Weight in Michigan's Metropolitan Areas." *American Journal of Public Health* 101, no. 9: 1714–20.

De la Rosa, Iván A. 2002. "Perinatal Outcomes among Mexican Americans: A Review of an Epidemiological Paradox." *Ethnicity & Disease* 12 (Autumn): 480–87.

DuBois, Ellen Carol, and Lynn Dumenil. 2012. *Through Women's Eyes: An American History.* 3rd ed. Boston: Bedford/St. Martin's.

Du Bois, W. E. B. 1899. *The Philadelphia Negro: A Social Study.* Philadelphia: University of Pennsylvania Press.

Duster, Troy. 2003. *Backdoor to Eugenics.* 2nd ed. New York: Routledge.

Ekland-Olson, Sheldon, and Julie Beicken. 2012. *How Ethical Systems Change: Eugenics, the Final Solution, Bioethics.* New York: Routledge.

Feagin, Joe R., and Karyn D. McKinney. 2003. *The Many Costs of Racism.* Lanham, MD: Rowman & Littlefield.

Ferber, Abby L. 1998. *White Man Falling: Race, Gender, and White Supremacy.* Lanham, MD: Rowman & Littlefield.

Filippi, Melissa K., David G. Perdue, Christina Hester, Angelia Cully, Lance Cully, K. Allen Greiner, and Christine M. Daley. 2016. "Colorectal Cancer Screening Practices among Three American Indian Communities in Minnesota."

Journal of Cultural Diversity 23, no. 1: 21–27.

Fixico, Donald L. 2000. *The Urban Indian Experience.* Albuquerque: University of New Mexico Press.

Freimuth, Vicki S., Sandra Crouse Quinn, Stephen B. Thomas, Galen Cole, Eric Zook, and Ted Duncan. 2001. "African Americans' Views on Research and the Tuskegee Syphilis Study." *Social Science & Medicine* 52: 797–808.

Galea, Sandro, Melissa Tracy, Katherine J. Hoggatt, Charles DiMaggio, and Adam Karpati. 2011. "Estimated Deaths Attributable to Social Factors in the United States." *American Journal of Public Health* 101, no. 8: 1456–65.

Gallet, Craig A., and Hristos Doucouliagos. 2017. "The Impact of Healthcare Spending on Health Outcomes: A Meta-regression Analysis." *Social Science & Medicine* 179: 9–17.

Glenn, Evelyn Nakano. 2010. *Forced to Care: Coercion and Caregiving in America.* Cambridge, MA: Harvard University Press.

Gorman, Bridget K., and Jen'nan Ghazal Read. 2006. "Gender Disparities in Adult Health: An Examination of Three Measures of Morbidity." *Journal of Health and Social Behavior* 47 (June): 95–110

Gould, Stephen Jay. 1981. *The Mismeasure of Man.* New York: W. W. Norton.

Gray, Simone C., Sharon E. Edwards, Bradley D. Schultz, and Marie Lynn Miranda. 2014. "Assessing the Impact of Race, Social Factors and Air Pollution on Birth Outcomes: A

Population-Based Study." *Environmental Health* 13, no. 4. doi:10.1186/1476-069X-13-4.

Green, Tiffany L., and William A. Darity Jr. 2010. "Under the Skin: Using Theories from Biology and the Social Sciences to Explore the Mechanisms behind the Black–White Health Gap." *American Journal of Public Health* 100 (suppl. 1): 36–38.

Guadagnolo, B. Ashleigh, Kristen Cina, Petra Helbig, Kevin Molloy, Mary Reiner, E. Francis Cook, and Daniel Petereit. 2009. "Medical Mistrust and Less Satisfaction with Health Care among Native Americans Presenting for Cancer Treatment." *Journal of Health Care for the Poor and Underserved* 20, no. 1 (February): 210–26.

Health Resources and Services Administration. 2015. "Sex, Race, and Ethnic Diversity of U.S. Health Occupations (2010–2012)." U.S. Department of Health and Human Services. Accessed Jun 2, 2017. https://bhw.hrsa.gov/sites/default/files/bhw/nchwa/diversityushealthoccupations.pdf.

Hertzman, Clyde. 2012. "Putting the Concept of Biological Embedding in Historical Perspective." *Proceedings of the National Academy of Sciences* 109 (suppl. 2): 17160–67.

Hosokawa, Michael C. 2012. "Please Don't." *Annals of Behavioral Science and Medical Education* 18, no. 1: 21–22.

Hubbard, Ruth, and Elijah Wald. 1999. *Exploding the Gene Myth.* Boston: Beacon Press.

Human Genome Project Information Archive.

2013. "About the Human Genome Project." Accessed December 30, 2013. http://web.ornl.gov/sci/techresources/Human_Genome/project/index.shtml.

Indian Health Service. 2017. "Disparities." Fact sheet, April. Accessed May 14, 2017. https://www.ihs.gov/newsroom/factsheets/disparities.

International Society for Ethnopharmacology. 2012. "Vision." Accessed December 25, 2013. http://www.ethnopharmacology.org/ISE_about_us.htm.

Jackson, Pamela Braboy, and David R. Williams. 2006. "The Intersections of Race, Gender, and SES: Health Paradoxes." In *Gender, Race, Class, and Health: Intersectional Approaches,* edited by Amy J. Schulz and Leith Mullings, 131–62. San Francisco: Jossey-Bass.

Jesudason, Sujatha, and Julia Epstein. 2011. "The Paradox of Disability in Abortion Debates: Bringing the Pro-choice and Disability Rights Communities Together." *Contraception* 84, no. 6: 541–43.

Korosec, Kirsten. 2017. "2016 Was the Deadliest Year on American Roads in Nearly a Decade." *Fortune,* February 15. Accessed June 19, 2017. http://fortune.com/2017/02/15/traffic-deadliest-year.

Lam, Bourree. 2014. "Who Stays Home When the Kids Are Sick?" *Atlantic,* October. Accessed May 14, 2017. https://www.theatlantic.com/business/archive/2014/10/who-stays-home-when-the-kids-are-sick/382011.

Lombardo, Paul A. 2008. *Three Generations and No Imbeciles: Eugenics, the Supreme Court, and* Buck v. Bell. Baltimore: Johns Hopkins University Press.

Martin, Emily. 2006. "Moods and Representations of Social Inequality." In *Gender, Race, Class, and Health: Intersectional Approaches,* edited by Amy J. Schulz and Leith Mullings, 60–88. San Francisco: Jossey-Bass.

Massey, Rachel. 2004. "Environmental Justice: Income, Race, and Health." Global Development and Environment Institute, Tufts University. Accessed June 2, 2017. http://www.ase.tufts.edu/gdae/education_materials/modules/Environmental_Justice.pdf.

McKeown, Thomas. 2014. *The Role of Medicine: Dream, Mirage, or Nemesis?* 2nd ed. Princeton, NJ: Princeton University Press.

McLaren, Lindsay, and Penelope Hawe. 2005. "Ecological Perspectives in Health Research." *Journal of Epidemiology & Community Health* 59, no. 1: 6–14.

Mora, Pat. 1984. *Chants.* Houston, TX: Arte Público Press.

———. 1993. *Nepantla: Essays from the Land in the Middle.* Albuquerque: University of New Mexico Press.

Morgen, Sandra. 2002. *Into Our Own Hands: The Women's Health Movement in the United States, 1969–1990.* New Brunswick, NJ: Rutgers University Press.

National Institutes of Health. 2015. "Risk Factors for High Blood Pressure." September 10. Accessed May 14, 2017. https://www.nhlbi.nih.gov/health/health-topics/topics/hbp/atrisk.

National Medical Association. n.d. "History." Accessed June 2, 2017. http://www.nmanet.org/page/History.

O'Donnell, Liz. 2016. "The Crisis Facing America's Working Daughters." *Atlantic,* February 9. Accessed June 15, 2017. https://www.theatlantic.com/business/archive/2016/02/working-daughters-eldercare/459249.

Olakanmi, Ololade. n.d. "The AMA, NMA, and the Flexner Report of 1910." Paper prepared for the Writing Group on the History of African Americans and the Medical Profession, American Medical Association. Accessed June 2, 2017. http://www.ama-assn.org/resources/doc/ethics/flexner.pdf.

Olshansky, S. Jay, Toni Antonucci, Lisa Berkman, Robert H. Binstock, Axel Boersch-Supan, John T. Cacioppo, Bruce A. Carnes, Laura L. Carstensen, Linda P. Fried, Dana P. Goldman, James Jackson, Martin Kohli, John Rother, Yuhui Zheng, and John Rowe. 2012. "Differences in Life Expectancy Due to Race and Educational Differences Are Widening, and Many May Not Catch Up." *Health Affairs* 31, no. 8 (August): 1803–13.

Ossorio, Pilar, and Troy Duster. 2005. "Race and Genetics: Controversies in Biomedical, Behavioral, and Forensic Sciences." *American Psychologist,* 60, no. 1 (January): 115–28.

Park, Lisa Sun-Hee. 2011. *Entitled to Nothing: The Struggle for Immigrant Health Care in the Age of Welfare Reform.* New York: New York University Press.

Parker-Pope, Tara. 2013. "Tackling a Racial Gap in Breast Cancer Survival."

New York Times, December 20. Accessed June 2, 2017. http://www.nytimes .com/2013/12/20/health/ tackling-a-racial-gap-in-breast-cancer-survival. html?_r=0.

Pollard, Kelvin, and Paola Scommegna. 2013. "The Health and Life Expectancy of Older Blacks and Hispanics in the U.S." Population Reference Bureau, *Today's Research on Aging,* no. 28 (June). Accessed June 19, 2017. http://www.prb.org/pdf13/ TodaysResearchAging28 .pdf.

Pollitt, Phoebe Ann 1996. "From National Negro Health Week to National Public Health Week." *Journal of Community Health* 21, no. 6: 401–7.

Randall, Alice. 2012. "Black Women and Fat." *New York Times,* May 6. Accessed June 2, 2017. http://www .nytimes.com/2012/05/06/ opinion/sunday/why-black-women-are-fat.html?_r=0.

Rasanathan, Kumanan, and Alyssa Sharkey. 2016. "Global Health Promotion and the Social Determinants of Health." In *Introduction to Global Health Promotion,* edited by Rick S. Zimmerman, Ralph J. DiClemente, Jon K. Andrus, and Everold N. Hosein, 49–64. San Francisco: Jossey-Bass.

Read, Jen'nan Ghazal, and Michael O. Emerson. 2005. "Racial Context, Black Immigration and the U.S. Black/White Health Disparity." *Social Forces* 84, no. 1: 181–99.

Repka, Matt. 2013. "Enduring Damage: The Effects of Childhood Poverty on Adult Health." *Chicago Policy Review,* November 27.

Robert Wood Johnson Foundation. 2011. "Race, Socioeconomic Factors and Health." Exploring the Social Determinants of Health, Issue Brief 6, April. Accessed June 4, 2017. http://www .rwjf.org/content/dam/farm/ reports/issue_briefs/2011/ rwjf70446.

Ruiz, John M., Heidi A. Hamann, Matthias R. Mehl, and Mary-Frances O'Connor. 2016. "The Hispanic Health Paradox: From Epidemiological Phenomenon to Contribution Opportunities for Psychological Science." *Group Processes & Intergroup Relations* 19, no. 4: 462–76.

Savitt, Todd L. 1982. "The Use of Blacks for Medical Experimentation and Demonstration in the Old South." *Journal of Southern History* 48, no. 3 (August): 331–48.

Saxton, Marsha. 2010. "Disability Rights and Selective Abortion." In *The Disability Studies Reader,* 3rd ed., edited by Lennard J. Davis, 120–32. New York: Routledge.

Schulz, Amy J., Graciela B. Mentz, Natalie Sampson, Melanie Ward, Rhonda Anderson, Ricardo de Majo, Barbara A. Israel, Toby C. Lewis, and Donele Wilkins. 2016. "Race and the Distribution of Social and Physical Environmental Risk." *Du Bois Review* 13, no. 2: 285–304.

Sedgh, Gilda, Rubina Hussain, Akinrinola Bankole, and Susheela Singh. 2007. "Women with an Unmet Need for Contraception in Developing Countries and Their Reasons for Not Using a Method." Occasional Report 37, Guttmacher Institute, June. Accessed February 13, 2015. http://www.guttmacher .org/pubs/2007/07/09/ or37.pdf.

SisterSong. 2013. "What Is Reproductive Justice?" Accessed February 13, 2015. http://sistersong.net/ index.php?option=com_ content&view =article&id=141.

Smedley, Brian, Michael Jeffries, Larry Adelman, and Jean Cheng. 2008. "Race, Racial Inequality and Health Inequities: Separating Myth from Fact." Briefing Paper, Opportunity Agenda and California Newsreel. Accessed June 2, 2017. http://www.unnaturalcauses .org/assets/uploads/file/ Race_Racial_Inequality_ Health.pdf.

Snyderman, Nancy. 2012. "North Carolina Budget Drops Payment to Forced Sterilization Victims." NBC News, June 20. Accessed December 30, 2013. http:// usnews.nbcnews.com/_ news/2012/06/20/12321330-north-carolina-budget-drops-payment-to-forced-sterilization-victims?lite.

Somerville, Siobhan B. 2000. *Queering the Color Line: Race and the Invention of Homosexuality in American Culture.* Durham, NC: Duke University Press.

Spanakis, Elias K., and Sherita Hill Golden. 2013. "Race/ Ethnic Difference in Diabetes and Diabetic Complications." *Current Diabetes Reports* 13, no. 6: 814–23.

Stone, Lisa Cacari, and C. H. Hank Balderrama. 2008.

"Health Inequalities among Latinos: What Do We Know and What Can We Do?" *Health and Social Work* 33, no. 1: 3–7.

Strauss, John, and Duncan Thomas. 2007. "Health over the Life Course." California Center for Population Research, November. Accessed May 8, 2017. http://papers.ccpr .ucla.edu/papers/PWP-CCPR-2007-011/PWP-CCPR-2007-011.pdf.

Striegel-Moore, Faith-Anne Dohm, Kathleen M. Pike, Denise E. Wifley, and Christopher G. Fairburn. 2002. "Abuse, Bullying, and Discrimination as Risk Factors for Binge Eating Disorders." *American Journal of Psychiatry* 159, no. 11: 1902–7.

Sue, Derald Wing. 2010. *Microaggressions in Everyday Life: Race, Gender, and Sexual Orientation.* Hoboken, NJ: John Wiley.

Sullivan, Louis W., and Ilana Suez Mittman. 2010. "The State of Diversity in the Health Professions a Century after Flexner." *Academic Medicine* 85, no. 2: 246–53.

Syme, S. Leonard, and Lisa F. Berkman. 2009. "Sociology, Susceptibility, and Sickness." In *The Sociology of Health and Illness: Critical Perspectives,* 8th ed., edited by Peter Conrad, 24–30. New York: Worth.

Tavernise, Sabrina, and Robert Gebeloff. 2013. "Millions of Poor Are Left Uncovered by Health Law." *New York Times,* October 2. Accessed June 1, 2017. http://www .nytimes.com/2013/10/03/ health/millions-of-poor-are-left-uncovered-by-health-law.html?pagewanted =all&mcubz=1.

Thomas, Stephen B., and Sandra Crouse Quinn. 1991. "Public Health Then and Now: The Tuskegee Syphilis Study, 1932 to 1972: Implications for HIV Education and AIDS Risk Education Programs in the Black Community." *American Journal of Public Health* 81, no. 11: 1498–505.

United States Holocaust Memorial Museum. n.d. "The Murder of the Handicapped." The Holocaust: A Learning Site for Students. Accessed December 28, 2013. http://www.ushmm .org/outreach/en/article. php?ModuleId=10007683.

Urban Indian Health Commission. 2007. *Invisible Tribes: Urban Indians and Their Health in a Changing World.* Seattle: Urban Indian Health Commission. Accessed May 14, 2017. https:// www2.census.gov/cac/ nac/meetings/2015-10-13/ invisible-tribes.pdf.

U.S. Bureau of Labor Statistics. 2017. "Occupational Employment and Wages, May 2016." Accessed June 1, 2017. http://www.bls. gov/oes/current/oes311011 .htm.

U.S. Department of Health and Human Services, Office of Minority Health. 2011. "Pathways to Integrated Health Care: Strategies for African American Communities and Organizations." Accessed June 4, 2017. http:// minorityhealth.hhs.gov/ Assets/pdf/Checked/1/ PathwaystoIntegrated HealthCareStrategiesfor AfricanAmericans.pdf.

Verma, Reetu, Samantha Clark, Jonathon P. Leider, and David Bishai. "Impact of State Public Health Spending on Disease Incidence in the United States from 1980 to 2009." *Health Services Research* 52, no. 1. doi:10.1111/1475-6773.12480.

Waldstein, Anna. 2010. "Popular Medicine and Self-Care in a Mexican Migrant Community: Toward an Explanation of an Epidemiological Paradox." *Medical Anthropology* 29, no. 1: 71–107.

Warner, David F., and Tyson Brown. 2011. "Understanding How Race/ Ethnicity and Gender Define Age-Trajectories of Disability: An Intersectionality Approach." *Social Science & Medicine* 72: 1236–48.

Washington, Harriett A. 2008. *Medical Apartheid: The Dark History of Medical Experimentation on Black Americans from Colonial Times to the Present.* New York: Anchor Books.

Weber, Lynn. 2006. "Reconstructing the Landscape of Health Disparities Research: Promoting Dialogue and Collaboration between Feminist Intersectional and Biomedical Paradigms." In *Gender, Race, Class, and Health: Intersectional Approaches,* edited by Amy J. Schulz and Leith Mullings, 21–59. San Francisco: Jossey-Bass.

Weng, Suzie S., and Jacqueline Robinson. 2014. "Intergenerational Dynamics Related to Aging and Eldercare in Asian American Families: Promoting Access to Services." In *The Collective Spirit of Aging across Cultures,* edited by Halaevalu F. Ofahengaue Vakalahi, Gaynell M. Simpson, and Nancy Giunta, 157–71. Dordrecht: Springer.

White, Kevin. 2009. *An Introduction to the Sociology*

of Health and Illness. Thousand Oaks, CA: Sage.

Williams, David R. 2012. "Miles to Go before We Sleep: Racial Inequities in Health." *Journal of Health and Social Behavior* 53, no. 3: 279–95.

World Health Organization 1996. "Traditional Medicine." Accessed December 25, 2013. http://www.who.int/inf-fs/en/fact134.html.

Zambrana, Ruth E., and Bonnie Thornton Dill. 2006. "Disparities in Latina Health: An Intersectional Analysis." In *Gender, Race, Class, and Health: Intersectional Approaches,* edited by Amy J. Schulz and Leith Mullings, 192–227. San Francisco: Jossey-Bass.